SH

To Laura

SHUT UP SARAH

MARION FIELD

*Love from

Marion Field*

Highland Books

GODALMING
SURREY

First published in 1996 by Highland Books,
Two High Pines, Knoll Road, Godalming, Surrey,
GU7 2EP.

Cover Design by Sally Maltby

British Library Cataloguing-in-Publication Data. A
catalogue record for this book is available from the
British Library.

ISBN: 1 897913 28 1

Printed in Great Britain by Caledonian International
Book Manufacturing Limited, Glasgow.

DEDICATION

DEDICATED TO
SARAH'S PARENTS

This is a true story. The events are real but the names and identifying details of the individuals have been disguised to safeguard their privacy and prevent any embarrassment to them or their families.

Contents

ACKNOWLEDGEMENTS

I feel greatly honoured to have been allowed to read 'Sarah's detailed diaries of her traumatic ordeal. Because the diaries have been used, it seemed appropriate to write the book in the first person. I am also very grateful to 'Sarah' for her help in writing this book and her patience in answering my questions.

Thanks are also due to her parents for letting us tell the story in the hope that it may help others who find themselves in a similar position.

I would also like to thank Deo Gloria Outreach for its continuing encouragement and Tim Harding, the Director, for writing the foreword.

FOREWORD

The story you are about to read will strike many as so bizarre as to defy belief. Sometimes harrowing, sometimes ludicrous, the situations in which Sarah finds herself, and the pressures to which she is subjected seem to belong to another world. In a sense they do for the Exclusive Brethren are increasingly ensuring that their daily paths overlap as little as possible with those of the rest of society. As you follow the vicissitudes of Sarah's teenage life, the question may well arise as to whether her case is not an isolated instance. Sadly there is strong evidence that such treatment is the norm for those who rebel or question the teaching they hear within this group; they too will undergo the same mental and spiritual tug-of-war as you will read of here.

For those who, like myself, have had past connections with the Exclusive Brethren, there is an added sadness to the story, for the Brethren movement in its origins was Godly, Biblically based and evangelistically motivated. It should be explained that there are various groupings within the Brethren movement and that the authoritarian group referred to in this book are those who followed the leadership of James Taylor Junior. In the last thirty five years there has been a steady movement away from the Biblical principles which guided the founding fathers in the nineteenth century and this drift has continued even since the events recounted here.

There can be no justification for publishing books which simply sling mud. Paul in 1 Corinthians chapter 13 reminds us that love does not gloat over evil. In retelling Sarah's story, Marion Field has sensitively avoided the temptation to sensationalise it.

I believe this book will serve two very valuable purposes. Firstly, it will help those who have neighbours or business contacts in the group to realise something of the pressures many are enduring. Perhaps another Bill and Janice will be able to offer a lifeline of friendship and hospitality to a young person struggling to decide whether to leave or stay. Secondly it may find its way into the hands of younger Brethren. It is my prayer that through reading it and hearing the other side of the story – not least sharing Sarah's discovery there are many thousands of other Christians in the 'world' - they will have the courage to make the break themselves, and encounter, perhaps for the first time, live Christianity.

If only a handful do so, Marion's work and Sarah's ordeal will have been worthwhile.

TIM HARDING

DIRECTOR, DEO GLORIA TRUST

Deo Gloria Outreach, an arm of the Deo Gloria Trust, is a non-denominational Christian organisation offering advice and support on a confidential basis to people encountering the type of problems described in this book.

- The address is:
  DEO CLORIA OUTREACH
  Selsdon House
  212/220 Addington Road
  South Croydon
  Surrey
  CR2 8LD
  Tel: 0181-651 6246 (24 hour ansaphone)

CHAPTER ONE

⌘

IT WAS AN ACCIDENT!

Be kind and compassionate to one another, forgiving each other, just as in Christ God forgave you. [Ephesians 4: 32]

"Look at her, sitting there in all her shame!"

"It's a disgrace to cut her hair and allow the devil to get in."

"Such a shame to see a young sister affected by sin."

"A terrible sin."

"She must be evil."

I sat in the Meeting Room, trying to hold my head up high and not let anyone see how afraid and upset I was. I'd hoped my headscarf would cover my short hair. Tears bubbled up behind my eyes as four hundred pairs of eyes stared accusingly at me. As the tears started to fall, I couldn't believe this was happening to me. I was only thirteen and I was being made to feel like a criminal. And it had all been a dreadful mistake.

At the time it had been exciting to have my hair cut, when I knew it was forbidden by the Brethren, but I'd only wanted the ends trimmed. How could I know my younger sister would be such a dreadful hairdresser and keep getting it wrong? The harder she tried to straighten it, the more she cut off. When she'd finished, I looked in the mirror. With horror I realised I had short hair – an unforgivable sin to the Exclusive Brethren, the very rigid sect with whom we worshipped. There were many groups of Brethren but the one to which we belonged had been led, before I was born, by Mr James Taylor, Junior, who had initiated many of the rules and regulations I found so difficult.

The Brethren dominated every aspect of our lives and anyone who deviated in any way from their very strict rules was in danger of being either expelled from the group or 'shut up'. The latter was a horrible fate based on a verse from the Bible where lepers were 'shut up' so they wouldn't contaminate anyone else. If one person in a Brethren family 'sinned', the whole family was 'shut up'.

To the Exclusive Brethren, as indeed to some other Christians, leprosy represented 'sin' so anyone who 'sinned' could expect the same punishment. I trembled as I thought I might be 'shut up'. I would have to stay in my room with no one to talk to except the brothers sent to lecture me on the evil of my ways and I wouldn't be able to go to any 'Meetings', as the services were called, until I'd 'repented' and learnt my lesson. I thought of the shame it would bring on my family and shivered in horror.

Male voices were shouting at me and hundreds of eyes were staring at me, some in disgust, some in sympathy. This Thursday evening was supposed to be a 'Reading Meeting' when a book of the Bible was usually studied. But it seemed a long time since anyone had explained the Scriptures to me. All they did was quote the verses which supported whichever narrow rule was currently of importance.

Today the reading was from the first book of Corinthians chapter eleven. 'It is a disgrace for a woman to have her hair cut.' Mr Bates roared this out and then turned to the brother beside him. "What do you say to that, Brian?"

Brian Forbes, shaking his head mournfully, responded as expected. "It's a terrible sin for a young sister to cut her hair and link herself with the evil world."

I couldn't stand it any more. This constant verbal battering almost made me believe the devil had got hold of me. I leapt up knocking over my chair. Blinded by tears, I ignored the gasps of horror behind me as I fumbled my way over other 'sisters'' knees to the door. Dragging it open, I slammed it behind me with all my might and then, gasping for breath, I started to run.

My headscarf had slipped off my head, my hair was blowing over my eyes and with my tear streaked face, I must have looked like the original mad woman from Bedlam.

Vaguely I was aware of the bemused gaze of passers by as I hurtled along the streets of the suburban town, where we lived, in an attempt to put as much distance as possible between me and my tormentors. At last I stopped because I had no breath left. What was the point of running? There was nowhere to go. They'd always catch me wherever I ran. I was trapped, trapped, TRAPPED.

My tears started again and I was wondering where to go when suddenly I heard footsteps.

"Sarah. Where are you? Sarah, come back."

Horrified, I realised one of the leaders of the Meeting, Mr Bates, was chasing me. I could hear him gasping for breath as he drew nearer. Wildly I looked round. I was standing near a telephone kiosk. Wrenching open the door, I crouched down inside but I was too late. He'd seen me.

"Sarah." He grabbed my arm but desperation gave me strength.

"I'm not going back. I can't stand it any longer," I screamed.

I pulled out of his grasp and ran back towards the 'Meeting Room'. Our car was in the car park and I headed for it. I knew it would be unlocked and once inside, I'd lock it and wait. Later I'd decide what to do. My fear gave me speed and I reached the car and flung myself into the back seat hurriedly locking all the doors. For the moment I was safe. Mr Bates rattled the door handles and shook his head mournfully at me but gave up at last and went back to continue the Meeting.

15

I quickly pulled on my headscarf – to be seen without one, even in a car park, was a 'sin' – and searched for a handkerchief. It was already soaked but I scoured my face with it and then slumped back and thought back over the past few days which had been the worst of my life. Why – oh – why had I asked Rachel to cut my hair?

After much pleading on the previous Friday evening, my parents had allowed my sister and me to stay at home rather than go to the Meeting. When they'd left, I'd asked Rachel to cut my uneven ends but I hadn't realised how difficult it would be for her. I shall never forget my parents' horrified faces when they came home and saw my shorn locks. Dad had shouted at me and Mum had burst into tears. On the following day there'd been a 'Fellowship Meeting' when Brethren from a wide area met together.

It had been awful! My friends wouldn't talk to me or even look at me and of course the Meetings had been about nothing but the verse in Corinthians where St Paul says women shouldn't cut their hair. They took everything he said literally and ignored the love that Jesus showed to people who'd done wrong. I wished he was here to help.

On Sunday I couldn't face going to the Meeting where I knew everyone would stare at me but I had to go to the Monday Prayer Meeting. Every brother prayed about nothing but my hair! Surely there must be more important things to talk to God about, I thought. But to them it was the burning issue of the day.

It seemed terrible that I, a child, should be considered so evil. They couldn't decide what to do with me. Should they forgive me or 'shut me up' because I'd brought 'shame on the Assembly'. I was sure Jesus would have forgiven me. They even phoned the 'Chief Priest', Mr Finch, in Australia to ask him for his advice.

"Ooh...just look at her hair."

A crash at the window jolted me back to the present and I glared at the faces of the small children who were crowding round peering at 'the sinner'. The Meeting had ended and the Brethren were flowing out into the car park. I noticed Ruth Bates smirking at me.

"How evil she's getting."

"I'd never think of cuttting my hair."

"I expect they'll shut her up."

"Go away!" I shrieked banging on the window but they only laughed. I pulled my headscarf over my eyes. Would this torment never end?

I hated the Brethren. Why didn't they let us have any happiness? We couldn't even go away for the day without getting permission from one of the 'priests'. Even going to the beach was considered 'evil'. How stupid! How could the beach and the sea that God created be 'evil'? I wished I'd been born into a normal family like my classmates at school.

The children had now disappeared and I grinned suddenly, remembering a day the previous summer. The Grays, a family with four small children, had come to one Sunday Meeting with bright red faces. It was

17

obvious they'd been to the sea the day before. I'm surprised they came because the Brethren talked about nothing else that day. Poor things. I knew how it felt to be 'picked on', I thought sullenly, glaring out into the darkness.

I wished I could leave the Brethren – but where would I go? I didn't know any one else and 'the world' frightened me. I'd lost count of the number of times I'd been told how 'evil' it was. Surely not everyone could be 'evil'; kind Mrs Hill, our neighbour, didn't look evil to me. I desperately wanted to escape but I thought sadly of the Brethren who had left; we'd been told over and over again they would be 'devoured by the world' and 'their souls would be lost forever'.

I hated everything. The clothes I had to wear were awful, too. We weren't allowed to wear jeans or trousers. Even when we went sledging, skirts had to be worn. These got in the way all the time and it was embarrassing to wear a long flowery skirt, when everyone else my age was dressed in jeans. I sighed. My life stretched before me in one long boring Meeting. Would I ever be able to escape?

"Sarah." There was a sharp tap on the window.

My eyes jerked open. Dad was trying to get in the car but I'd locked all the doors. I leaned forward to unlock them. Mum got in the other side. Neither of them spoke as Dad started the car and we drove away from the sullen accusing eyes of the children who were still pointing at me.

At last I could bear the silence no longer. "Well - what's going to happen to me?" I demanded. I was annoyed my voice quavered and I knew I was about to cry again.

"The Brethren have decided to forgive you – this time. They feel you've suffered enough. Mr Bates said he's sure you've learnt your lesson so there's no need to 'shut you up'."

I felt as if a great weight had been rolled off me. Why was I so relieved? I couldn't understand it. I wanted to leave but I knew I had to stay because everyone 'out there' was wicked. I felt in a complete muddle; I disagreed with things the Brethren said and I knew they hated me. But the thought of leaving home and never seeing my family again made me feel sick. My brothers, Richard and Tim could be 'pains' but we did have good times and Rachel was my best friend.

No I didn't want to leave – not yet at any rate. I gave a shuddering sigh and wiped my eyes.

"They won't shout at me any more?"

"No."

But I found the sniggers and the constant comments after the Meetings just as bad. I didn't go out until the following Sunday for the 'Supper' as it was called. Saturday night I didn't sleep well; the thought of facing all those accusing eyes again kept me awake. When five o'clock came, I told Mum I was ill so she'd let me stay at home but she wouldn't listen. Why did they have to have the 'Supper Meeting' so early? I was sure no other churches had their services at six o'clock in the morning! Mum had once told me it was because the Lord Jesus would visit us first!

It was dark and cold as we drove along. No one else was about. Only the Brethren got up at five every Sunday morning! We drove into the car park and walked towards the square brick building. The only windows were slits near the roof and it looked like a prison. It was a prison, I thought, fighting down panic. I was trapped.

In silence we filed into the building which was just as depressing inside. Rows of tiered chairs formed a circle with a table in the middle. On this were a loaf of bread, a large glass of red wine and a basket for the collection. The men sat in the front rows and the women sat behind.

Everyone turned round as we entered and stared at us. I knew my short hair was the attraction. I slunk in and sat between Mum and Rachel. I didn't pay much attention to what was said. It was the same every week. I took a piece of bread from the loaf when Mum passed it to me and then passed it on to Rachel. I'd been 'breaking bread' as long as I could remember. It was considered a special moment for the 'assembly' when babies reached out their hands to take the bread. No one had ever explained to me what it was all about. I didn't really understand much at all. When the wine came, I took a sip and hurriedly passed it on, wiping my mouth on my handkerchief.

When all the brothers had prayed and all the sisters had given out hymns in the structured sequence, there was the usual shuffling and I knew my torture was about to start. Mrs Wheeler, who was sitting close by, turned her head. She looked like a witch with her grey hair streaming down her back under her navy blue headscarf. My heart flipped.

"How nice to have you with us, Sarah dear," she cackled. "I'm sure your hair will grow quickly and you'll soon look like a beloved sister again."

I scowled. I didn't want to look like 'a beloved sister'. No doubt there'd be the same comments after every Meeting. We drove home for a quick bacon and egg breakfast before going back to the 'Room' for the next Meeting at nine o'clock. Sunday was all Meetings. There were five of them. This one was a Bible reading, followed by a preaching, but I never learnt anything – just heard about rules, rules and more rules.

When it was over, I sidled up to Vicki Harris and Katie Farmer who were talking together. They were supposed to be my friends but when I was close to them, they stopped talking and turned away. I knew they'd been discussing me. I was beginning to feel very isolated. I decided the best way to avoid any more embarrassment was to lock myself in the toilet. Everyone would be talking for hours and ignoring me. I might as well be 'shut up', I thought, rebelliously. It was definitely better to stare at four blank walls than be ignored or lectured about my 'sin'.

I wished I'd got my diary with me. If I wasn't able to write down my thoughts, I'd go mad. Surely I couldn't really be so 'evil'; someone must care for me. Nobody really understood me, not even my family. I knew they loved me, but their loyalty to the Brethren made them judge me too. But I knew Jesus still cared for me whatever I'd done.

How I wished I'd never been born into such a life. But both my parents had been brought up in the Brethren and it was their whole life. They were so convinced the Brethren were always right. But I was getting more and more disillusioned. I sighed and glanced at my watch. The time was going so slowly and I was very uncomfortable. Hoping no one would wonder why the toilet door was closed for so long, I stretched out my legs and shut my eyes trying to imagine myself a million miles away surrounded by friendly people who were all being kind to me. But my imagination wouldn't work and tears squeezed out under my eyelids and spilled down my cheeks.

Angrily I brushed them away. I would not cry. How dare the Brethren hurt me so much. No one knew how unhappy I was. I blew my nose loudly on some toilet paper.

"Sarah." It was my sister. "Sarah, where are you? We're going now."

"Just coming," I called, trying to sound cheerful. I flushed the toilet so it looked as though I'd been locked into the 'smallest room' for a reason. I'd pretend I'd been talking to friends all the time. I opened the door and Rachel stared at me.

"Are you all right?" she asked sympathetically.

"Of course I'm all right," I snapped. But I wasn't. I wondered if I'd ever be happy again. I couldn't imagine it.

It was time for the 'break'. It sounded like school! In fact I'm sure the Brethren had more rules than we ever had at school.

"We're going to the Bates," Mum announced.

I groaned. Ruth Bates was my age and no doubt she wouldn't speak to me for fear of linking herself with 'the world'. There'd be more hours of isolation.

"I don't feel well. Can I go home?" I hissed at Mum.

"Everyone's talking about you enough already without you refusing to go out," Mum scolded. "Come along. You get on with Ruth, don't you?"

Sometimes I did but now nobody wanted to know me. We drove to the Bates in silence and found all the sisters crowded into the kitchen, busily preparing mountains of food for the brothers who were already seated and drinking whisky. I hated the way the men always expected to be waited on hand and foot. I know St Paul said wives should be 'subject' to their husbands but surely that didn't mean the brothers lived like lords and the sisters like slaves.

"What can I do to help?" I asked, walking into the kitchen. Everyone looked embarrassed and once again I felt like an outsider. I didn't want to pass food round to the men but I knew I would have to. I knew, too, what everyone was thinking. "Poor Sarah. What a tragedy."

It was a good feast. There were baked potatoes, salad, ham and egg rolls and baskets and baskets of cakes. I munched into yet another slice of chocolate cake.

"Enjoying it? You look as though you are." Chris Bates wandered over and perched on the arm of my chair. I stared at him in amazement. It was very unusual for a 'young brother' to speak to a 'young sister' – and certainly one as 'sinful' as I was.

I nodded, my mouth full, and hoped the rest of the Brethren wouldn't notice he'd spoken to me. At least he acknowledged that I existed. I began to feel a little more cheerful as we chatted together.

There was another Meeting at half past twelve but this time Mum let me stay at home. I was so exhausted with all the 'hair drama' that I went to bed and fell asleep straight away.

It seemed no time at all before Mum was calling me to get up to go to yet another Meeting. It started at four o'clock and Brethren from other Meetings were there too. The 'Room' was packed. As usual we were late and I held my head high as I walked in knowing everyone was staring at me. I tried to pretend I didn't care what they thought of me.

For once I tried to concentrate on the preaching. There were three preachers all talking about the same subject – 'control in the household'. I looked in sympathy at Dad – a dig at him, I thought. He was the 'head of the household' and should have kept me in order!

At last it was the turn of the last preacher, a boy of sixteen or seventeen. It was becoming the custom for a very young brother to preach last. This was the first time Bill James had spoken and I could see he was nervous. He didn't say anything new but there were hearty 'Amens' from all the brothers as he sat down.

When we got home, a lovely smell of roast beef was drifting around the house. Mum had put it on before we'd left.

"I do hope it's not burnt," she worried. "We're not usually as late as this."

"It smells all right," I said, my mouth watering. After all it was several hours since I'd eaten!

The meat was beautifully tender and only the edges were a bit black. A sledge hammer would have been useful for some of the roast potatoes but what could you expect when dinner had to be instantly ready after the Meeting for any visitors who might come?

"It looks delicious," beamed Dad picking up the gravy boat and dousing the meat with the contents.

"John!" Mum sounded horrified. It wasn't gravy! It was chocolate sauce! "I'm so sorry, dear. I couldn't find another jug so I used my old gravy boat. Here's the gravy." She handed it to him.

Dad was not amused. "I don't think I want a chocolate sauce sandwich," he said sarcastically.

"Let me scrape it off," I offered, giggling. I spooned the thick gunge on to a spare plate and handed dad back his plate. "There. Most of it's off. It'll probably add to the flavour. You've probably started a new fashion. Roast beef and chocolate sauce."

As we all sat down together to the delicious dinner and an evening of family 'togetherness', I wondered how I had ever thought I could leave this secure world.

CHAPTER TWO

✥

I CAN'T BELIEVE IT!

Jonathan said, "My father has made trouble for the country. See how my eyes brightened when I tasted a little of this honey."
[1 Samuel 14: 29]

Things didn't improve on the Brethren front. I was still an 'outcast' although I hadn't been 'shut up' or 'withdrawn from' – the Brethren term for expelling people from the group.

Sometimes I wished they *had* thrown me out. At least I would have been able to start a new life. No I wouldn't, I reminded myself; everyone 'out there' was evil. I was afraid to get friendly with any of the girls at school because they were 'worldlies' and I didn't want to be contaminated by 'the world', did I?

They didn't want to be friends with me either because I was 'peculiar'. I had to wear a headscarf to school and with my new short hair, it looked ridiculous. I heard some of my classmates sniggering as I dumped my bag on my desk on Monday morning and slouched into the chair. I caught Ruth Bates' eye across the room and glared at her. I knew she wouldn't waste any sympathy on me. I put out my tongue.

I was too miserable to concentrate on my lessons. What was the point? I'd have to leave school at sixteen and work for one of the Brethren 'firms'. We weren't allowed to go to College or work for 'worldly' people. I could hear Mr Brown's voice droning on about how the Rift Valley in Africa was formed but I couldn't care less.

At the end of the lesson I slouched out, carefully avoiding Ruth. There wasn't any light at the end of the tunnel. My life was a black hole and I was gradually being sucked into the middle. No doubt eventually I'd disappear altogether. Dawdling along, lost in my thoughts, I suddenly realised the corridor was almost empty. Bridget Soames from my class was just disappearing into a classroom. I hurriedly followed her and dropped into an empty seat at the back. I'd forgotten what lesson I was supposed to be in!

"Turn to St Luke chapter ten and verse thirty. You'll find it on page sixty eight."

I froze at the sound of the teacher's voice. Tiny fingers of fear crept over my body and I glanced fearfully towards the front of the class. Miss Jones, dark and pretty, was holding an open Bible and waiting for the class to stop turning pages. I was in an R.E. lesson! How had I got there? We weren't allowed into

R.E. lessons in case we were taught something the Brethren disagreed with. While the rest of the class went to R.E., I was supposed to be in the Library with all the other 'PBs' (Plymouth Brethren). (Some of the original Meetings had been held in Plymouth and the name had stuck although it didn't only apply to the Exclusive Brethren.)

Hot and cold flushes swept over me. I couldn't draw attention to myself by leaving. I'd just have to stay – and not listen.

"Haven't you got a Bible?" Miss Jones was standing beside me. Before I could stammer anything, she turned to the girl beside me. "Share yours with her please, Bridget."

She didn't even seem surprised to have an extra pupil. How odd! I glanced round the room, recognising most of the pupils. At least it was my own year and no one would know - would they?

Bridget had found the place and pointed to it and I followed as the teacher read out the story of the Good Samaritan. I knew it, of course, but to me it was just a story. I'd never thought about what it meant.

"What can we learn from this?" asked Miss Jones when she'd finished it.

Bridget put up her hand. "We shouldn't refuse to help anyone just because they're different from us."

"Yes, Jesus was teaching something important through telling a story. Now look at St John chapter four and verse seven." It was the story of the Samaritan woman at the well. "Are there similarities?"

"He didn't condemn her for what she'd done and he talked to her although he was a Jew and she was a Samaritan."

I hadn't been able to 'switch off'. I was fascinated. I'd learnt more in a few minutes than I had in months of Meetings. There was a happy atmosphere in the room and for the first time it dawned on me that there were other Christians in the world besides the Exclusive Brethren. I was sitting next to one and Miss Jones had to be one. I gazed at her enviously. Could she really be a Christian with her colourful smart clothes, discreet make up and short hair? But I knew she was and the seeds of doubt inside me started to sprout a little.

When the bell went, my heart started pounding again. I hoped no one would see me coming out of an R.E. lesson. I hid behind Bridget as we left the room. Thank goodness there were no 'PBs' in sight as I strolled towards my next lesson.

"Sarah, where have you been?"

Oh horrors! Ruth Bates had sneaked up behind me. I whirled round, acting surprised.

"What? Oh I wasn't well. I went to the sick room," I lied. She looked at me suspiciously and then linked her arm in mine. Ugh! She felt like a prison warder but I didn't dare shake her off. That would have been another black mark against me.

After the next lesson it was break and Ruth stuck to me like a limpet. Katie turned up too and there we were – three long haired idiots wearing headscarves marching round the playground. I felt so stupid. Katie wasn't as bad as Ruth. She wore nice clothes and her hair always shone. Ruth just looked a mess. Her hair was always greasy and her clothes were so old fashioned. She behaved as though she was at least forty.

Katie felt a bit like I did. We never told anyone we didn't have a television. Whatever would they have thought? If anyone talked about a programme, we looked interested and agreed we'd enjoyed it and then no one was suspicious.

As we passed the gym, Jason Coley shouted out, "Here come the three heavies. Want a haircut, me hearties?"

I felt myself blushing but forced myself to ignore him. Ruth just giggled. Stupid thing! Fortunately the bell went and he went off in the opposite direction.

At afternoon break Bridget came over to me.

"Like a doughnut, Sarah?" she asked, holding it out. "My Mum put two in for me and I can only manage one."

I'd opened my mouth to thank her when I saw Ruth Bates' beady eye on me. Sadly, I shook my head.

"No thanks, Bridget. I'm not really hungry. But thanks anyway."

I daren't accept anything to eat from someone who wasn't 'one of us'. I liked Bridget but I was a bit afraid of 'worldlies' and didn't want to get too friendly with one. After all, they were all 'evil', weren't they? Only the Brethren were right – weren't they?

I sighed and tried to sort out my feelings. My mind felt like a crumpled shirt that needed ironing. The R.E. lesson had made me think. There were an awful lot of 'worldlies' compared with the Brethren. Surely they couldn't all be 'wicked'. Bridget seemed really nice.

I had another shock when I walked home after school. As usual I was dawdling and for once Ruth wasn't clinging on to me. I took a short cut to make sure she didn't catch me up. It was one of those lovely Autumn days and I felt glad to be alive. I wanted to smile at everyone. The only person available was an old man working in his garden. He'd just taken a rest and as I passed, I couldn't help grinning at him.

He smiled back and said, "Hullo."

I'd always been taught not to talk to strangers and of course, in the Brethren that meant anyone not 'in the Meeting'. But I didn't care. It was broad daylight and there were plenty of houses around.

"Isn't it a lovely day?" I said.

"Beautiful. I want to tidy this up before the bad weather comes."

"Your garden's lovely. You must work hard at it."

"I enjoy it and you know the saying, 'You're nearer God's heart in the garden than anywhere else on earth'."

I didn't know it and it seemed an odd thing for him to say. Strangers didn't usually talk about God when they'd just met, did they? I smiled, slightly embarrassed.

"Just going home from school, are you?" he asked, "I've seen you before."

I was a little surprised but I supposed he was lonely and liked to watch people passing by.

"What's your name?" he asked.

"Sarah."

To my astonishment his expression changed and he looked really sad. "I've got a granddaughter called Sarah," he told me. "She must be about your age but I never see her."

I wondered why. He seemed such a nice old man. What a shame he didn't see his granddaughter. I couldn't think of anything to say to comfort him. He was staring at me quite hard and I was getting embarrassed again. I wanted to leave him but I couldn't without seeming rude.

After a pause he said, almost shyly, "Could you tell me your other name, please?"

I couldn't think why he wanted to know but it wasn't a secret.

"Foster," I told him.

To my horror I realised there were tears in his eyes.

"My name's Foster too," he said and he turned away and walked towards the house.

I stared after him. I couldn't believe it. My brain went numb. Then I got angry – really angry. I couldn't wait to get home.

"Mum," I shouted as I burst in, tossing my bag on the floor. "Mum, where are you?"

She was in the dining room arranging some flowers. "What on earth's the matter, Sarah? Do you have to shout like that?"

I took a deep breath. "Mum, have I got another grandfather still living?"

She didn't need to answer. I'd often read about people 'blanching' but I'd never seen it happen before. She collapsed into a chair and I moved to stand over her.

"Why wasn't I told?" I demanded, through clenched teeth. I'd never been so angry before. For nearly fourteen years I'd had a grandfather and hadn't known about him. We lived on the outskirts of a town and our 'village' was no tiny chocolate box one but it wasn't that large and I couldn't believe that no one had ever mentioned him.

Mum shook her head. She was still white and I could see her hands were shaking but I didn't care. I wanted some answers.

At last she said, "We used to visit him when you were little. You must remember."

"But why did we stop? I don't remember anything about him."

"You'll have to ask Dad."

"I'm asking you," I snarled, still standing over her.

She looked frightened and for a moment I felt ashamed but I had to know. She was saved by the sound of the front door opening.

"There's Dad now. Go and ask him. It's his father." She pushed me out of the way and I hurtled into the hall to bombard Dad with the same question.

He turned away to shut the front door but I could see he was shaken. Good, I thought!

"Come and sit down, Sarah." He led me into the lounge and I sat down facing him.

"Well?"

"It all happened a long time ago – before you were born. Your grandfather deliberately went against the wishes of the Brethren and they had no option but to 'withdraw from' him."

"What had he done?" I demanded, not taking my eyes off his face. He wouldn't look at me.

"He refused to accept the new ministry that Mr Taylor introduced. He set himself up against the leaders of the day and was wilfully disobedient." He sounded as though he was reciting a lesson!

"I suppose you mean he didn't agree with the idea of not eating a meal with anyone not in the Brethen," I said sarcastically.

"That, among other things. It all happened a long time ago, Sarah." Something suddenly struck him. "Why are you asking about him?"

"Because I met him today and I shall talk to him whenever I see him. He's really lonely and I think it's disgraceful you won't have anything to do with him."

Leaping up, I burst into tears and rushed upstairs to mourn for all those lost years. For the rest of the week I avoided the short cut. I wanted to see my grandfather again and I knew I would but first I had to sort out my feelings. I felt so confused. Fancy having a granddad living near me and not being allowed to see him. It was so ridiculous.

The following Sunday was a disaster. I couldn't help thinking of my poor grandfather and wishing he was here with us. But then there was a problem with my other grandad who lived with us and I forgot grandfather Foster because I was so embarrassed. At the 'Supper Meeting' in the morning grandad gave out a hymn. There was no organ or piano so we always sang unaccompanied and whoever gave out the hymn usually started it. Grandad began to sing but he'd made up the tune so of course no one knew it. He sang the hymn right through by himself! I wanted to crawl under the seat! When he'd finished, he looked really cross because no one else had joined in and he slammed his hymn book shut.

I noticed Ruth Bates was about to give out a hymn so I got in first and gave out one. She glared at me and shut her hymn book. We started to sing and I hoped everyone would have forgotten about Grandad's 'solo'.

Monday was an improvement. In fact it was a really good day. It had been a week since I'd first met my grandfather and today I was determined to see him again. I had no intention of obeying Dad and ignoring him. I wanted to make up to him for all those lost years. He wouldn't be able to see his other grandchildren but at least he'd have me. How sad he must have been all those years. Ruth was away from school so I walked home alone and took the short cut.

I was so relieved to see Grandad Foster in his garden again. I wondered if he'd been there every day during the previous week. I started to feel guilty at snatching a precious week from him.

"Hullo," I said shyly.

He beamed. "I was hoping you'd come. I've got something to show you. Wait here." When he came back, he had some photographs in his hand. He handed them to me. "That's your Aunt Jenny who lives in New Zealand and these are your cousins. They're coming to England soon."

I didn't even know I had an aunt – or cousins. There was a lump in my throat and I couldn't say anything. I looked at some more photos.

"Who's that?" I asked, pointing.

"That's your Uncle Adrian and his wife, Rosemary. They live near here too."

"Have they got children?"

He nodded. "Two. Tessa's about your age and Mike's bit older."

Wow! It was really weird suddenly acquiring relatives you didn't know about.

37

He gave me the last photo. "That's your grand-mother. It was taken a few days before she died. Doesn't she look happy?"

I gazed at the white haired lady who looked back at me, smiling. Yes she did look happy – but she must have been so sad at not being able to see all of us. I felt so sorry for my grandfather. He must be lonely without her.

The next day he was waiting for me again but Katie was with me so I was a bit embarrassed. He had his camera and he asked if he could take a picture of me to send to New Zealand. I didn't know what to say. It was so ridiculous that my own grandfather couldn't take my picture without a fuss. If I'd been by myself, it wouldn't have mattered.

"I'll have to ask Dad if it's all right," I said at last.

He looked so hurt I wished I hadn't been such a coward. "I'll see you tomorrow then," he said and went into the house.

"Why does he want to take your picture," asked Katie, puzzled.

"If I tell you, will you promise faithfully not to tell anyone?"

"Of course. You know you can trust me."

I hoped I could. "He's my grandfather," I told her, "but I didn't know anything about him till I met him by accident last week."

"Was he 'withdrawn from'?" asked Katie shrewdly.

"Of course he was," I snapped. "I think the whole thing's so pathetic. Why on earth do the Brethren think they're so special? There must be other Christians in the world."

"But they haven't got 'the Light'," replied Katie trotting out the well worn phrase. "You mustn't say things like that. Someone might hear you."

"I don't care," I said crossly. "I'm fed up." I ran ahead of her. I couldn't be bothered to talk to her any more.

The next day I was alone and grandfather had his camera again. This time he didn't ask.

"Stand still," he ordered and before I knew what was happening he'd snapped the camera. It was so embarrassing. I glanced round to make sure no one had seen. But I was quite glad he'd done it. I hadn't asked Dad because he'd probably have said, "No."

"When are my cousins coming over from New Zealand?" I asked.

"I'm hoping they'll be here soon."

"Oh good." I couldn't wait. I was determined to meet them and I wanted to hear all about New Zealand. Perhaps I'd be able to go there one day. It would be wonderful to escape from the Brethen. But they'd probably follow me and drag me back!

"I've just had a letter from your cousin, Lucy. You can read it if you like."

I glanced round again. Katie had said she'd wait for me round the corner and there was no one else near.

"All right." I waited impatiently for him to return and was glad I had because the letter was really interesting and my cousin sounded so nice. I couldn't wait to meet her.

When I handed the letter back, he said, "I'd like to give your some money to put in your savings account."

"Oh no!" I exclaimed in horror. "Oh dear. I didn't mean that. It's very kind of you but..."

"I give money to all my other grandchildren so why shouldn't I give you some, too?" He sounded quite cross.

"Well...it's ...it's very kind of you. Er... thank you very much."

"I'll give it to you tomorrow when I get my pension."

"Thank you," I said hurriedly. "I'll have to go now. Katie's waiting for me."

Fortunately she hadn't heard anything although she did complain she'd been waiting ages. The next day grandfather gave me ten pounds which was really sweet of him. I asked him for Lucy's address so I could write to her.

I felt really good as I walked home. God had been good to me recently. I'd asked him to tell me which way I should go – whether I should stay with the Brethren or leave and go to my cousins in New Zealand – if they'd have me. That night I read my Bible hoping to find my answer but it wasn't there.

I didn't see Grandfather Foster the next day but when I got home, I had a shock. Dad was already home and looking very solemn.

"Come in here, Sarah," he said sternly. "I hear you've been talking to your grandfather."

I blushed. "So what?" I muttered.

"Ruth Bates saw you and reported it. You're not to talk to him any more Sarah and you're to walk home with Ruth every day."

I might have known! And I thought I'd been so careful. My mind whirled. I knew I wasn't going to obey him but a row wouldn't help at the moment. I had to think.

"All right," I said sullenly. "But I think it's cruel. He's an old man and he's lonely. How would you feel if none of us would have anything to do with you?"

"If you continue to see him, Sarah, you'll be 'shut up' and then you won't be able to see any of your family. You wouldn't like that, would you?"

I stared at him, horrified. Would the Brethren really do that to me? I couldn't bear the thought of losing my family. After dinner I said I was going for a walk. I had to tell my grandad what had happened although I was terrified I'd be found out. My heart was beating loudly as I forced myself to walk up to his front door.

"Sarah!" he exclaimed when he opened the door. "How lovely to see you. Will you come in?"

"No, no, I can't. Someone told the Brethren I've been seeing you and I have to walk home with Ruth

41

every day so I won't be able to talk to you. But I'll give you a wave behind my back – like this." I demonstrated. "If I can get rid of her, I'll talk, but I'll have to be careful."

"You poor little thing," he said sympathetically and I almost cried.

"I'll have to go now. 'Bye."

All the way home, my legs were shaking. I knew what the Brethren were doing was wrong but I was so afraid of them. I was terrified they'd take it out on my family – 'shut them up' or 'withdraw from them'. I couldn't bear it. What was going to happen to us all? I couldn't take much more of this fear.

CHAPTER THREE

✠

MARRIAGE PROPOSAL

*Be strong and take heart all you who hope in
the Lord. [Psalm 31:24]*

For some time after Ruth 'sneaked' about my
grandfather, I tried to keep a low profile. Underneath I
was simmering but I didn't want to cause any trouble.
If I did, it would affect my whole family. That was the
awful thing. I managed to speak to Grandad Foster
occasionally but it wasn't easy and I always felt sick
afterwards in case I'd been seen.

The Meetings were still as boring as ever. They
always talked about the same things and most of the
time they didn't seem to have anything to do with the
Bible. One depressing Sunday at the beginning of
January, I read the whole of Revelation during the
Meeting. It was much better than listening to Tony
Bates going on about how much better the Brethren
were than everyone else. It was fascinating reading

about what was going to happen in the future. I was sure it wasn't written just for the Brethren!

When the Meeting was over, I felt a tap on my shoulder. I turned round. Mrs Bates was sitting behind me.

"You weren't paying attention, Sarah. I was watching you."

Shouldn't she have been concentrating on the Meeting?

"I was reading the Bible," I snapped.

"You should have been listening to the Ministry, Sarah. It's very important."

"More important than the Bible?" I dared to ask.

She didn't answer that, of course. "There's no need to be rude, Sarah," she said, sounding hurt. I turned away feeling cold shivers go over me. Did the Brethren really think that what they said was more important than God's Word, the Bible? Surely God would not allow them to go on with this – wickedness.

The next day we went back to school after the Christmas holidays and it was really awkward because everyone was talking about what presents they'd had for Christmas. We didn't keep Christmas and never had special Meetings to celebrate it. This puzzled me as it was Christ's birthday but Dad explained it was because we remembered his birth all the time and so didn't need a special occasion. I wished we kept it. I felt so envious when everyone else was talking about it. I was terrified Ruth would tell everyone we didn't keep it and I hoped no one would ask me what I had had. But of course they did.

"Oh nothing much, " I replied airily. "Just clothes – and money mainly and some little things."

Well I had bought some new clothes and I'd had my pocket money so it wasn't really a lie and no one seemed suspicious, fortunately. I saw Ruth giving me her usual disapproving glare but I ignored her. She was the embarrassment of my life. I hated walking round with her all the time. She was like a little pet dog following me – only there was nothing 'pettish' about her. Bridget came up to me at break time.

"Did you have a nice Christmas, Sarah?" she asked.

"Yes thank you," I said politely glancing over my shoulder at my 'pet'.

"My parents gave me a dog. I'd wanted one for ages. He's gorgeous – a little black and white terrier. He's ever so affectionate. I hated leaving him behind this morning. I think he'd have liked to have come with me."

"That's nice," I said, turning away so she couldn't see the tears that were ready to attack my cheeks. I glared at Ruth who was smirking. I loved animals and I wished I could have a pet dog but we weren't allowed pets. Apparently if we became too attached to a pet, we'd lose sight of God. How stupid. God made the animals too, didn't he?

However there was a 'let out' clause to this 'rule'. The only reason you could keep an animal was if you were going to eat it eventually! Ugh! As if you could eat a 'pet' you'd grown fond of.

But I remembered this as I listened to Mr Brown droning on about sheep farming in New Zealand. An idea started to germinate in my brain but I couldn't act on it until the following half term. On Tuesday during the holidays we sometimes went to the weekly cattle market held in the nearest large town. It was one of the 'treats' we were allowed. I was always fascinated by the hustle and bustle of the auctions and I could pretend I was a lady farmer come to sell my sheep.

"Can we go to the cattle market today, please, Mum?" I pleaded as we were having breakfast on the Tuesday of half term.

Mum buttered her toast and looked thoughtful. "Well as it happens, I've got some shopping to do," she said. "All right we'll go but I don't want to say long."

"O.K. Thanks." I gave Mum a quick hug and hurtled upstairs to finish dressing. How I wished I could wear the jeans I'd hidden at the bottom of the drawer but I knew that would be asking for trouble.

No one else wanted to go so Mum and I set off alone. The town was always busy on market day and it was lunch time before we got there. I was hungry but of course we couldn't go into a restaurant to eat with 'the world'. Mum had made some sandwiches so we ate them in the car before we went shopping.

"You've got an hour, Sarah," Mum informed me as we finished them. "Don't be late back."

"I won't. I promise."

I ran off heading for the market. I loved the cattle smell and the crowds. No one knew me here and it was unlikely I'd meet any brethren. I leant over the sheep pen. They were just being herded out to be auctioned and I followed the crowd to the tent. There were some darling little lambs too. One of them was completely black.

"Poor little thing," I thought. "I wonder if he feels like I do sometimes."

I watched him frisking around as lots were called and farmers waved their papers or shot up their hands. I wondered who would buy him.

To my surprise he was sold by himself – probably because he was black.

"Who'll start me at two pounds for this beautiful specimen?" intoned the auctioneer. "Thank you, Sir. Any advance on two pounds?"

The bidding crept up and when it got to ten pounds, I raised my hand. I wasn't sure whether I'd intended to bid or not but the auctioneer thought I had.

"Any advance on ten pounds? No? Going, going, gone."

I couldn't believe it. I was in possession of a little black woolly lamb. I climbed through the fence to collect him and handed over ten pounds – all my worldly wealth. He felt so soft and tiny as he lay in my arms and baa-ed at me. I didn't think of the consequences.

I sauntered back to the car wondering how I was going to tell Mum. She was sitting waiting for me and her response was predictable.

"I've bought a lamb," I announced nonchalantly. She seemed to have lost her voice which was probably just as well. "I'll sit in the back and hold it. It's all right, Mum. The Brethren can't complain. We'll say we're going to eat it."

"Sarah!" she croaked at last. "We can't keep it. Where will you put it?"

"In my bedroom," I said promptly.

"But..."

"It'll be all right, Mum, really."

We didn't speak on the way home and I hugged my new pet. I was going to call him Frisky. I knew we were going to be great friends. We were certainly not going to eat him.

When we got home, I put a piece of red ribbon round his neck as a collar and attached another piece to it to use as a lead. I carried him out of the house and set him down and he trotted off with me following. He was better than a dog.

The next day I bought a proper collar and lead for him and wrote his name and address on the collar. Proudly, I walked him down the road. Our neighbour, Mrs Hill, was out for a walk with her dog. Frisky was frightened of the big labrador so I picked him up.

"What sort of dog is he, dear?" Mrs Hill asked, puzzled.

I giggled. "He's not a dog. He's a lamb."

"Oh – I see." She gave me an odd look and dragged her pet away.

We all grew very attached to Frisky. Dad made him a shed but he grew too big for it and wandered round the garden. Mum wasn't very pleased when he ate all her flowers! At three months old he was a stately black sheep – far too big for us to keep.

"What are we going to do with him?" Mum worried.

"Skin him and eat him," suggested Dad.

"Don't be so horrid." I started to cry. "We can't eat him. He's lovely."

Richard, my older brother, looked sympathetically at me across the table. I hadn't eaten anything. I felt sick at the thought of lovely Frisky who'd just been licking my face, being killed and eaten. I'd never eat lamb again.

"I'll take him to the market for you, tomorrow," Richard offered.

"All right." I ran upstairs and flung my arms round my doomed pet. His lovely black wool was soon soaked with my tears as he nuzzled me.

The next day, I watched through a blur as Richard loaded Frisky into the back of his car and drove off. I cried all day but at least I wouldn't be eating my pet.

I got the giggles in the Reading Meeting on Tuesday. It really was so ridiculous. Brian Forbes started going on and on about 'separation from the world' until I could have screamed. Then he said that Brethren who lived in semi-detached houses and had 'worldly' neighbours had to have insulation put between their houses to insulate them from the 'world'! How pathetic!

"Those who live in semi-detached houses," he droned, "must not entertain as it's wicked not to be separated from 'the world'."

It was really difficult not to laugh out loud. He looked just like a ferret and all the brothers in the front row were nodding their heads so enthusiastically it was a wonder they didn't drop off!

I could hear his voice droning on and on even when I was in bed. I got to sleep eventually and was startled to hear Mum say, "What are you doing here, Sarah?"

I thought I was dreaming but I woke up and found myself in the kitchen! I'd sleep walked! I'd never done that before. It was quite frightening and I had trouble sleeping after that. I was afraid of where I might go the next time.

The following Sunday Cathy Vine from Wales was at the Meeting with her new husband. I hadn't seen her since her marriage and I was pleased when she came straight over to speak to me.

"How are you, Sarah?" she asked.

"Fine, thanks. How's married life?"

"Great. We've got a lovely house. You must come and stay for a weekend, Sarah."

"I'd love to," I said, thrilled. I wasn't going to pass up a chance like that. Cathy had always been friendly to me.

"Would you like to come next week? We'll pick you up at the station."

"I'll have to ask Mum and Dad." I raced off.

Fortunately they agreed after they'd checked with the 'priests' and I was so excited the next week I was even nice to Tony Bates. I had a lovely weekend and the best part was Sunday because Peter Glover was at the Meeting. I'd seen him before and I liked him. I kept sneaking glances at him when he wasn't looking. He looked really nice in a black leather jacket and once when he caught me looking at him, he smiled and I blushed. I'd have liked to talk to him after the Meeting but I was too shy. However, I decided to send him a Valentine's card. I saw a good one which said, 'Hope to see you soon' but I didn't get it after all. I found another and sent it to him.

When I returned from Wales, I got a shock. A new 'rule' had been introduced. No one was now allowed to go away for a holiday or even for a day. The only exceptions were brothers who went to 'take' Meetings in different parts of the country and those who were invited to go to the monthly international Meetings in Bristol and the three day Meetings which were held several times a year in different countries. I couldn't believe it. I was so pleased I'd just been away but the thought that I'd never be able to go again made me feel really trapped.

I hoped I might be invited to go to some three day Meetings or even to Bristol but with my 'black sheep' record the chances seemed pretty remote. The three day Meetings acted as a marriage market. 'Marriageable' sisters were invited so young brothers could choose a bride. But the couple weren't allowed to communicate or even kiss each other until the wedding day. It didn't seem to me a very good basis for a happy marriage.

Marriage was something that occupied the Brethren's minds a great deal. After all there wasn't much else for girls to do. We weren't allowed to go on to higher education or get decent jobs. All that was open to us was to marry young and have crowds of babies to swell the numbers of the Brethren. All the Brethren had large families and there were gatherings all over the British Isles, in Europe and in the rest of the English speaking world. It was almost unheard of for anyone from 'outside' to join us. We rarely had any 'converts' in spite of the regular preachings in town centres on Fridays. If someone had expressed an interest, they'd have had to have many meetings with various brothers before being allowed to join the Exclusive Brethren. I didn't want my children to grow up in this stifling atmosphere. I wanted them to be free – as I wanted to be free.

Laura Stevens was getting married and she wanted to make a really beautiful wedding dress from very expensive material. But the Brethren found out about it and were really sarcastic in the Meeting about the waste of money. Brides always had to make their own wedding dresses. I couldn't think why they were making such a fuss about Laura's when to buy one would probably have cost hundreds of pounds.

Brian Forbes went on and on about it. Then he started talking about child bearing and how important it was to start a child as soon as you were married. He went into disgusting detail and I wanted to crawl under the chair. I felt so sorry for Laura.

But the next Sunday I forgot about her when my name was read out as one of the 'suitable sisters' to go to the French three day Meetings in Lyons during the Easter holidays. I was thrilled. I'd never been abroad before. But I knew the Brethren had an ulterior motive. If I was 'promised' to a 'respectable young brother', perhaps I'd settle down and not be such a rebel. I knew I was far too young to be thinking of marriage. I hadn't even left school. But the three day Meetings would be a new experience and I'd get away from the local brethren who were making me so cross.

I knew it would be a busy time because the sisters had to wait on the brothers hand and foot. At least I could cook. That was one thing I'd learnt as we never knew how many people would be turning up for Sunday dinner. We always had to be prepared.

None of my family was going and I didn't know anyone else which I thought was a good thing. The Brethren chartered a plane and on Thursday evening, Mum drove me to Heathrow Airport where I met up with all the other Brethren who were going to France for the same reason. Several other girls were being decanted at the same time. You couldn't miss them. They all wore dark headscarves with hair straggling down their backs and old fashioned clothes. I felt so embarrassed walking through the airport surrounded by hundreds of headscarves. I was sure everyone was staring at us and laughing.

I was going to stay with my pen friend, Nicole. I had several pen friends from different countries as writing letters was something the Brethren did allow us to do. Letters were taken to the monthly Meetings in Bristol and pen friends were arranged through brothers from different countries. The three hour 'chats' in the car park after the Meetings were even more important than the Meetings themselves, it seemed to me.

Nicole's English was quite good but her parents didn't speak any and as my French was practically non existent, we had to communicate by signs and smiles. It was quite funny.

I was very tired and was glad to go to bed in the room I was sharing with Nicole. It was quite a big house and I thought they must be quite well off. I slept well and I didn't sleep walk – thank goodness.

The next day we woke early and had to cook in readiness for the Break. Then we had a lovely breakfast of French bread with lashings of butter and jam before driving to the first Meeting. It was crowded and I had plenty of time to look around to see if there were any good looking boys. That was often the only thing that kept me from going mad with boredom in the Meetings. I wondered which one would propose as that was why I was there. It seemed really medieval.

The Meeting was very long and it was in both French and English. There were crowds of people there and the singing, which was all in French, was even worse than at home. I noticed one or two young men eyeing me but I didn't see anyone I really fancied. In the Break we were kept busy serving the food. We hardly had time to eat anything ourselves but I felt really privileged passing the food to some of the 'important' brothers.

By the evening I was exhausted and could hardly keep my eyes open in the Meeting. Then I realised one young man was persistently staring at me. I stared back. He wasn't bad looking but he was quite old – at least twenty three.

He came back to Nicole's house afterwards.

"I think Claud likes you," Nicole whispered to me as we took the freshly baked croissants out of the oven.

"Who?" I asked pretending not to know who she meant.

She giggled and jerked her head towards him as we carried the food into the living room. When the brothers had eaten their fill, we cleared up and I was surprised when Claud followed me into the kitchen. I was standing by the sink preparing to wash up and he put his plate on the draining board.

"'Ullo, Sarah," he said.

I dropped a plate and spun round blushing furiously.

"Hullo," I said.

"I see you later." He drifted out.

I wondered if I'd had my first proposal! He squeezed next to me in the car and after the Meeting he came over to me. He couldn't sit with me as the brothers always sat in the front and the sisters in the rows behind.

"You are from England, Sarah?"

"Yes. And you?"

"I live near here."

"Do you often go to three day Meetings?"

"Many times."

After that he followed me around. Whenever I turned, he was there.

"He trying to find bride for long time," Nicole told me that night when we were in bed. "He find many girls but all too closely related so no. So I think now he – 'ow you say? – set his heart on find one now. And I think he choose you. You say 'yes'."

I pretended to be asleep. I had no intention of becoming his 'last hope' but no one was going to know that yet.

The next day Claud was still around and finally he cornered me after the morning Meeting before the Break.

"Sarah, you will marry me?"

I couldn't decide whether it was a question or a statement!

I giggled. "I don't know, Claud. I hardly know you."

"But we get to know. Yes? I write to you."

"All right."

I knew he would be happy to wait two years if I said, "Yes". Then we wouldn't be allowed to see each other until the wedding. How ridiculous! Word soon spread and the local Brethren became really interested in me as I looked like becoming a new addition to their locality. Claud and I were even allowed to go to a Break together and talk to each other! Our new 'relationship' made the three day Meetings much more interesting but I had no intention of marrying him.

By the time the Meetings were over, I was exhausted. It had been a very hard time. We'd been up at six in the morning to cook and often it had been after midnight before we went to bed. I was relieved to get home and let Mum cook for me.

Claud wrote me several letters over the next few weeks but I didn't reply. Then he wrote again demanding to know when I would marry him. I took the letter to school and showed Vicki. She gazed at me in awe.

"Wow! Aren't you lucky? Your first proposal. What are you going to do about it?"

"Say 'no', of course. I don't want to marry – ever."

She looked shrewdly at me. "You'll change your mind. After all there's not much else to do, is there?"

I sighed. She was right. We weren't allowed to have careers like our classmates because we couldn't continue with our education. My excitement at receiving my first proposal of marriage faded. That night I wrote a diplomatic reply to Claud's letter and posted it quickly before anyone could try to persuade me to change my mind.

Of course the news that I'd refused a proposal of marriage was soon known in my own Meeting and provided yet another black mark against me. It was the last time I was ever invited to any three day Meetings abroad.

A few days later Katie phoned to tell me she'd seen Peter in Bristol. I was really jealous but then she said she'd been talking to his sister and Beth had said that Peter really liked me.

"Beth said she told him he was 'cradle snatching' but he said he didn't care; he'd wait for you."

"I don't believe you. You're making it up." I knew my cheeks were pink. Peter was older than I was but I did like him. Now if it had been him instead of Claud.......

"I'm not. It's true. Honest."

I was so happy that I danced all round the house and Mum wondered what was the matter with me. But I wouldn't tell her. I dreamt about Peter. The next day I discovered Katie had told Ruth Bates about him and I was really annoyed with her.

I'd forgotten about the Valentine card I'd sent him but apparently he'd guessed who it was from! He sent me a beautiful necklace which I had to hide. Then one night when I was alone in the house, he phoned. I felt myself go hot all over.

"Would you like to go out, sometime?" he asked.

"I'd love to," I said straight away. I was really happy inside. The Brethren wouldn't approve of course. I knew he was a 'rebel' like me. We should get on well! He'd got a car so he said he'd pick me up on the corner where no one would see us. It was horrid having to be so deceitful.

"I don't know if I can get away," I said. "Mum watches me all the time. It's awful not being allowed to do anything on my own."

"Can't you say you're babysitting or something?"

"I'll try." I put down the phone. It might not be too difficult. I often baby sat for various sisters and I always got on well with their kids.

We were still on holiday from school so I told Mum I was going to the town with Katie. I hoped she wouldn't turn up at my house while I was out. Peter was waiting for me when I arrived and I couldn't help looking round to see if there were any Brethren in the vicinity. There weren't fortunately.

"Where are we going?" I asked.

"Surprise." He took his hand off the wheel and took hold of my hand and my inside felt as though it was melting. Was I falling in love with him?

We went to a cinema! I'd never been in one before and I was terrified. I'd always been told they were 'dens of iniquity'. I looked round to make sure there were no lurking brothers as we went in. Inside the darkness made me feel I was going into hell and my heart was pounding so loudly I was sure no one would be able to hear the film. I stared, mesmerised, at the screen.

Tom Cruise was playing the lead and I soon became totally absorbed in the life of the characters on the silver screen. When it finished, I still felt part of it and it took a real effort to drag myself back to the present. Peter put his arm round me. When he kissed me, it was bliss. I felt excited and happy but then guilt surfaced again.

I knew Mum and Dad would be furious if they knew where I'd been and at a recent Meeting Tony Bates had given a long lecture about boys and girls not talking to each other. How were we supposed to get to know each other? I knew it had been aimed at me as he kept looking at me and I often talked to the boys after the Meeting. They were much easier to talk to than girls. Why didn't Tony Bates realise we were just friends.

But I thought Peter and I might become more than that. We started to see each other a lot and I became more and more fond of him. I discovered he was very 'naughty' and often went to pubs as well as cinemas and restaurants. His rebelliousness was part of his attraction for me. I'd found a kindred spirit. He was older that I was but I decided I preferred older men even though I'd turned down my first proposal of marriage from one.

When I got home from school the next day, I was in a rebellious mood. Ruth had been even worse than usual and I was fed up. Shutting myself in my bedroom, I burrowed in my underwear drawer and unearthed the small store of make up I'd surreptitiously bought over the past few months.

Carefully I put eyeliner on my eyes and darkened my eyebrows. Then I put rouge on my cheeks, mascara on my eylashes and finished off my efforts with lipstick. Peering at myself in the mirror, I felt on a real 'high'. It was as if I'd become a superstar with the first sweep of the mascara!

From the wardrobe, I pulled out my boring navy skirt and found the pair of jeans I'd carefully hidden. I pulled them on and topped them with a 'freaky' pink jumper I'd bought in a sale. Surveying myself in the mirror, I thought I looked quite 'normal'.

Just then I heard the front door and knew Mum had come in. I waited until I heard her go into the kitchen and then sneaked out and round to the garage for my bike. I hurtled down the path and out into the road. It would be dark soon but I didn't care. The wind rushed past my face and I pretended I was a 'normal' girl out for a cycle ride. Then an awful thing happened. I'd ridden up the road leading to the school. As it didn't lead anywhere, I was sure I wouldn't meet any 'PBs'. When I saw a boy coming towards me, I thought it was someone from school but to my horror, when I got closer, I saw it was Chris Bates, Ruth's brother.

Putting my head down, I zoomed into a nearby alley. I'd nearly got to the end of it when – horror of horrors – the Forbes family went past. I held my breath and hoped they hadn't seen me. I'd had enough excitement for one night so I turned home. I was almost there when I saw Tony Bates just ahead of me. I swerved off to go another way home and was so relieved when I reached home, I almost didn't see Dad in the driveway just getting out of his car. If I'd been a little earlier, I'd have been caught! Whew!

I waited till he'd gone inside and then sneaked round to the garage to put my bike away. Then I rushed upstairs hoping I'd be able to change and wash my face before anyone saw me. My heart was pounding so loudly, I was sure they'd be able to hear it downstairs and I was all fingers and thumbs as I tore off my jeans. I'd hardly washed my face and put on my skirt when there was a knock at the door and it was Katie. She and her mother had come to visit.

Although she wasn't really happy about things in the Meeting, she wasn't such a rebel as I was and I knew she wouldn't have approved of my escapade. She'd probably have told her mother who'd have told mine and then the Brethren would have been told and I'd be made to feel like a criminal.

In spite of my escape, I was still feeling rebellious on the following Sunday. My eyebrows were quite dark but I used an eyebrow pencil to make them a little darker and hoped it wouldn't notice. Then I dusted a tiny spot of rouge on to my cheeks and used a very pale lipstick. Would I get away with it? I must be mad, I thought. Why ask for trouble?

Mum and Dad didn't notice but I was sure Ruth Bates did. She kept giving me very odd looks during the Meeting so I decided I'd better wash my face during the break.

I took my make up to school with me the next day and put some on. Katie came in while I was doing it and, of course, was horrified.

"Sarah," she gasped. "What are you doing?"

"What does it look like?" I asked adding the final touches.

"You know we're not allowed to wear make up. It's 'worldly'."

"Everything's 'worldly'. I'm fed up with it. Promise you won't tell, Katie."

"Oh all right."

Secretly I thought she'd like to try some but she was afraid. She wasn't such a rebel as I was. Fortunately Ruth was away again. She'd certainly have sneaked on me. None of the teachers said anything. They were probably too busy to notice. But some of the boys were looking at me and that made me feel good.

I was still feeling adventurous when I got home. The 'freebie' had arrived so I sat down to browse through it. I looked through the advertisements to see if there was anything I fancied although I knew I wouldn't be allowed to do anything.

Then I saw it. 'Home help required. 4.30-6.00 weekdays. Two small children. Would suit schoolgirl.'

I read it again. Dared I? It would be great to meet other people. Why not? The house was still quiet so I ran upstairs and found some writing paper. It was a box number so in my best writing I said how suitable I'd be for the job and how I loved children – which was quite true. I couldn't find any stamps but I knew there was a stamp machine by the post box in our road so I grabbed some coins and ran out of the house.

I'd hardly got back when Mum arrived.

"You look flustered, Sarah," she remarked. "What's the matter?"

"Nothing," I lied. "We had a hectic game of hockey this afternoon – mixed."

Mum looked disapproving., "Isn't that dangerous?"

"Of course not," I scoffed. "It's much more fun. It's really tame with only girls."

She didn't say any more and I started to worry in case I got a reply to my letter. However I was often up early and for the next few days I was up even earlier to intercept the post. There was nothing and by the end of the week I decided I hadn't been successful. Then on Monday there was a letter for me. I put the other letters – mostly bills – on the hall table and rushed upstairs, tearing open the envelope.

Dear Sarah,

      We would very much like to meet you and discuss the job we advertised. Could you drop in to see us on Wednesday after school? We live not far from your school. The address is at the top.

              Yours sincerely,

              Janice Hawes

I couldn't wait for Wednesday and it was very hard to keep it to myself. After school on that day I spent ages in the cloakroom combing my hair and making sure I looked smart. I also wanted to avoid dear Ruth who was still sticking to me like a leech. I hoped she'd get bored with waiting for me and leave. I didn't want Katie around either. I liked her but I didn't really trust her. She always talked before she thought so I decided it was better not to tell her anything.

Ruth and Katie had both gone when I came out of the cloakroom and I walked quickly to my destination making sure no one was following me. When I reached the house, I had another quick look round and then marched up the drive and rang the bell. I could hear children playing inside.

"Sarah, how nice to see you. Do come in." Mrs Hawes was tall and pretty. She'd tied her fair hair back in a pony tail and she looked about eighteen but I knew she must be older than that.

Shyly I followed her in and two pairs of eyes stared solemnly at me.

"This is Edward. He's nearly five and Caroline's two. Say 'hullo' to Sarah."

They mumbled a greeting and Mrs Hawes laughed. She asked me some questions about how I got on with children and what experience I'd had. I felt completely at home but also guilty—as usual. Nice as she was, Mrs Hawes was still a 'worldly' and I was beginning to think I'd made a mistake.

I was wondering how to escape when she said, "We used to live next door to a Mr Foster in Lilac Drive. Would he be related to you?"

I went hot and cold. "He's my grandfather," I muttered. "But I only met him recently."

She nodded but didn't comment. "Well Sarah, I'm sure we'd get on really well. The job's yours if you'd like it."

A battle was going on in my mind. I did want it – more than anything else but I hated being deceitful. Could I face yet another battle if the Brethren found out? On the other hand I might be able to see more of my grandad. I looked up, still not sure what to do. Mrs Hawes was looking straight at me. Suddenly I realised she knew all about me. I sighed with relief and smiled at her. Yes it did seem right and – I might even be able to talk to her. I took a deep breath.

"Thank you," I said. "I'd like to work for you."

"Good."

"But...." I decided I'd better be honest. "My parents don't know. I – I – don't think they'd approve."

She was silent for a moment. Then she said, "I don't want to pressure you, Sarah. Perhaps you could talk your parents round."

I wouldn't tell them, I decided. Somehow I'd hide it from them. They disapproved of everything I did and this wouldn't be any different. But I couldn't tell Mrs Hawes that. I stood up.

"I'll try," I said. "When would you like me to start?"

"Monday?"

"That'll be fine."

On Monday I told Mum I was going to Katie's to do my homework and I'd stay for tea. Katie wasn't too pleased to be 'used' but after grumbling all day, she finally agreed.

I escaped my bodyguard again and took the short cut, humming to myself. Things were looking up, I thought. The sun was shining and the birds were singing. Skipping up the path of the Hawes' house, I rang the doorbell.

The door opened immediately. Had I come to the wrong house? The lady who'd opened the door certainly wasn't Mrs Hawes who was tall and slim. This lady was plump and dark but she was smiling at me. To my astonishment, before I could think of anything to say, she pulled me into the house and hugged me.

"Hullo, Sarah. It's so lovely to meet you at last. I'm your Aunt Jenny from New Zealand."

CHAPTER FOUR

✳

A MEETING IN BRISTOL

Cast your cares upon the Lord and he will sustain you. [Psalm 55:22]

I couldn't believe it. She led me into the front room and sat me down on the sofa.

"I'm Lucy's Mum," she said.

I nodded. My voice seemed to have disappeared and tears were streaming down my cheeks. She hugged me again and that made me cry even more. I don't think I'd ever cried so much in my life.

Edward appeared in the doorway and stared at me. Then he ran off and I heard him calling to his mother.

"She cry, Mummie. Why she cry?"

His voice reminded me I was there to work and I tried to compose myself.

"I'm sorry," I hiccuped.

"It's all right, dear. Cry as much as you like." I realised Aunt Jenny was crying too.

At last we composed ourselves and looked at each other. It seemed too good to be true. At last here was someone who would understand my feelings. I could talk to her without feeling disloyal.

"How long are you staying?" I croaked.

"About a month. I hope we'll be able to see something of each other."

"I hope so, too."

"Sarah, I want you to promise me something. You know we live in New Zealand. If you ever decide to break away and you want to come to us, you would be very welcome to stay as long as you like."

"Oh thank you, thank you." I hugged her. "One day I will – I'm sure."

We talked for ages and then Mrs Hawes brought us in a cup of tea. "Don't worry about the children today, Sarah," she said. "You've got a lot of catching up to do with your aunt."

We had. Until recently I hadn't even known she existed! I'd also acquired three more cousins as well as Lucy.

"Lucy and the two boys were born in England," Aunt Jenny told me. "Mary's the only one who was born in New Zealand. She even speaks with an accent."

"I can't wait to meet them." I mopped up my eyes with some tissues Mrs Hawes had thoughtfully provided and took a sip of tea. It was very soothing and I realised why people in shock were always given tea.

We talked for ages but eventually I had to go before Mum and Dad became suspicious. But I knew I'd see a lot of her before she went back.

The next Sunday it was quite difficult to keep my mind on what was going on. I'd seen Aunt Jenny several times but we hadn't been able to talk much as I'd had to look after the children. But it was enough just to know she was there and understood my problems.

My mind usually wandered and today I had a lot to think about. Some day I was definitely going to New Zealand to meet all my cousins. I didn't know how but I was sure it would happen somehow.

After the 'Supper' we went to the Bates for the 'Break'. I had to sit on a sofa squashed between Mrs Wheeler and her crony Miss Ellis, spitting on me as they talked across me as if I wasn't there!

When I finally prised myself away from them, Katie grabbed me.

"I've got something to tell you, Sarah," she giggled.

"What?"

"Clifford Strand wants to know when you're coming to a fellowship meeting again. He wants to talk to you."

"That creep!" I gasped. "I hate him."

"Well he likes you. He's been telling everyone he's going out with you."

"He's lying," I said furiously. "I wouldn't go out with him if – if -." Words failed me.

"Keep your hair on. I'm only repeating what he said. How was I to know you felt like that?"

"Well you know now," I growled stalking off. I was so angry. I hoped Peter hadn't heard the silly gossip. I was sure he wouldn't believe it.

I phoned him in the evening and we talked for at least an hour. I really liked him. He didn't believe the rumour about me and Clifford. I was so relieved.

When I put the phone down, I discovered my older brother, Richard, was hovering behind me. I went hot and cold. At the last three day Meetings in Bristol, he'd met Liz and proposed to her. She'd accepted him and he'd been working very hard to prepare his house for his bride. All young brothers were expected to buy a house as soon as possible even if they weren't engaged. I'd always got on well with Richard but I knew he didn't approve of Peter and I didn't want a row with him.

"Come in here, Sarah. I want to talk to you."

I followed him into the lounge which was empty and sat down. I knew what he was going to say.

"You're getting quite friendly with Peter, aren't you, Sarah?"

I felt colour creeping over my face and was furious with myself.

"Sarah?"

"Yes," I muttered.

71

He sighed. "You know you're not allowed to go out with anyone until you're married."

"It's such a stupid rule. How am I going to get to know someone if I can't talk to them?"

"The Brethren know what's best for you, Sarah." I gritted my teeth. How often had I heard that? I knew it wasn't true but I wasn't going to argue. "Promise me you won't see him again, Sarah."

I gasped. I should have seen it coming.

"I can't. I – I – think I'm in love with him." Tears squeezed out of my eyes.

"Oh, Sarah." He sounded so sad.

I jumped up and put my arms round him.

"Don't worry about me, Richard. I'll be all right. And I hope you and Liz will be happy."

"I'm sure we will."

"Do you think Liz will ask me to be a bridesmaid?" I'd never been one and it was one of my ambitions.

He looked embarrassed. "I – I – don't know."

The next Saturday we all went to dinner with Liz's family. She lived in Devon so it was a long journey and I was pretty tired when we got there. We didn't sit down to the meal until a quarter to five. Afterwards Richard and Liz disappeared. I knew they'd gone for a walk and was sure they'd get in a few kisses! How wicked!

Liz looked a bit flushed when she came back.

"Would you like to see my wedding dress?" she whispered to me.

"I'd love to."

We went upstairs to her bedroom and she opened the wardrobe and took it out. It was absolutely beautiful. She tried it on and looked really lovely in it. It was white silk with a tight bodice and high collar. Round the bottom were little bows and the long sleeves were puffed. She'd made it herself, of course.

"You are clever," I said enviously.

She didn't ask me to be a bridesmaid. I thought she'd probably heard gossip about my 'worldly' ways and I felt sure she didn't approve of me.

As it happened none of our family went to the wedding. I couldn't believe it. A new 'rule' was introduced just before the day. A wedding in future was to be only 'a local affair'. The only 'family' that now mattered was the local Brethren. They were our 'brothers and sisters' and natural relationships were no longer important. Family occasions like weddings and funerals would now only be attended by the 'local family' – the local Brethren. If you happened to go to the Meeting where the event was taking place, you could go. But if not, you weren't allowed to travel. The rules got more and more stupid.

Richard and Liz were married in her Meeting Room in Devon so we were banned as we weren't 'local'. Only one photograph of the bridal pair was permitted so we weren't even able to keep a record of the wedding. We were eventually allowed to see the picture but it wasn't very good.

The Brethren were doing a very good job of breaking up families I thought as I sobbed into my pillow on the day that should have been such a happy one for our family. Richard was the first of us to be married and it was heartbreaking not to be allowed to go to his wedding. It was particularly hard on my parents. We'd always been such a close family. Wherever was this all going to end? What other horrendous ideas would the Brethren dream up to destroy family relationships?

Soon after this I had something else to worry about. I'd been getting a really sore throat and one day I was so ill at school, they phoned Mum. I could hardly swallow and it was affecting my breathing.

Mum rushed me to the doctor and before I knew what was happening I was in hospital. My tonsils had to come out! I couldn't wait to get rid of them. When I came round from the operation, it was such a relief to be able to swallow and breathe properly although my throat was still sore.

I enjoyed my stay in hospital. All the other patients in the ward were much older than I was and they were really sweet to me. But there were some embarrassing moments. One afternoon I'd just come back from the bathroom and was walking slowly back to my bed when the lady in the bed opposite me called to me.

"Put the TV on will you, love, seeing as you're up."

I froze. I glanced quickly at the 'wicked' black machine in the corner and half moved towards it. Of course we weren't allowed to have one or to watch it and the array of buttons bewildered me. I had no idea how to switch it on. What was I to do?

It seemed ages before my brain caught up with the rest of me and I clapped my hand to my mouth.

"Sorry," I mumbled bolting out of the ward. "Have to go to the loo."

I escaped and hid until I thought someone else would have switched it on. Creeping back, I peered in. Thank goodness. It was on and all the patients were staring at it. None of them noticed me as I crept back to bed and buried my head under the blankets. I mustn't watch it, must I? It was evil – so the Brethren said.

At last my curiosity got the better of me and I peeped over the blankets. I glanced at the door to make sure I hadn't got any unwelcome visitors and then turned my attention to the screen. I was hooked! It was a travel programme about New Zealand and I watched, fascinated, as bungi jumpers leapt off a bridge, swinging precariously at the end of what looked like a piece of elastic. I wondered if I'd ever have the courage to do that if – no – when I went to New Zealand.

Although televisions were banned, I suddenly remembered a Meeting when I'd been about eight. Prince Charles had just married Lady Diana Spencer and, of course, it had been televised. I giggled as I thought back. About half the members of our Meeting had 'confessed' to having watched the wedding in shop windows. I remembered that even Chris Bates, who'd been about ten at the time, had 'confessed'. Of course the sisters didn't confess out loud. They told their husbands who announced their 'sin'. I wondered if the 'priests' had 'forgiven' them but I couldn't remember anything else.

Flocks of Brethren came to visit me in hospital. They took me into a side ward to talk so we wouldn't be 'contaminated' by the 'world' in the ward. If they were there at meal times, I ate in the side room. But if they weren't, I ate with the others in the ward, keeping a careful eye on the door to make sure no unwelcome guests appeared.

I recovered quickly and when it was time to leave, the doctor suggested to my parents that I should go away for a little holiday to recuperate. Of course, Tony Bates had to be consulted and he wouldn't let me go. I was furious – particularly as I wanted to go to Wales to stay with Cathy again.

"It's a stupid rule," I stormed at my parents. "Why do they have to give us permission? It's nothing to do with them."

"Everything's to do with them," said Dad grimly. "You can't go, Sarah, and that's that."

I went up to my room and cried for ages; it hurt my throat but I didn't care. Then I had another idea. Perhaps the Brethren would let me go to Bristol for one of the monthly meetings. If Peter could get invited too, we could meet.

To my delight I was invited to the next Bristol Meeting and, with a lot of persuasion, Peter was finally invited too. He rang me up.

"I can't talk for long, Sarah, but I'll be going on Wednesday. I'll hide the car in the bushes behind the car park. Do you know where I mean?"

"Yes. I'll see you there after the Meeting."

"We can go into Bristol city. They always talk for hours after the Meeting. They'll never miss us."

"Great. I can't wait."

Mum and Dad didn't go so I had to go with Mr and Mrs Bates. Ruth hadn't been invited so I was glad about that but I would have preferred different travelling companions.

It was a warm June night. We drove into the car park and then I followed Tony Bates and his wife into the large prison-like building. I shivered in spite of the warmth. It felt so claustrophobic. I sat with Mrs Bates on one of the tiered seats at the back of the hall. The brothers always sat in the front rows with the sisters behind. Down below us was a platform where the important brothers would sit and in front of this were three empty rows. Before the Meeting started names would be read out and those 'good' brothers who'd been chosen would troop down to the front and sit on their VIP seats.

The Meeting was supposed to start at eight but I knew it wouldn't. The Brother who was leading it was always late – just to show his authority over the rest of us. It was half past eight before Mr Marks, flanked by two henchmen, marched in. One of his companions pulled out a list from his pocket and read out the favoured brothers. Of course, Tony Bates' name was there. He looked like a cat that had swallowed the cream as he took his place with the elite. Ugh!

I saw Peter come in but I was careful not to catch his eye. I didn't pay too much attention to the Meeting. I was too excited about meeting him afterwards. It was about half past ten before we shuffled out. I managed to lose Mrs Bates in the crowd and slipped out of the back entrance. There were so many people there, I was sure no one would notice me. They didn't.

When I was outside, I walked quickly through the crowds already chatting in groups in the car park. I wondered if the neighbours complained. The noise would go on till after midnight. Peter's car was there and he was waiting for me.

"Hullo." We kissed quickly and then he said, "Quick lie on the floor in the back, Sarah, and pull that rug over you so no one will see you."

I giggled as I tried to arrange my legs in a comfortable position. I pulled the rug over my head.

"I'm ready." My voice was muffled and I banged my head on the door as the car shot forward. It was hard to breathe and I was getting cramp but it was worth it.

"Right." The car slid to a halt. "You can get out now."

I pulled off the rug and eased my cramped legs out of the door.

"Ouch. My foot's gone to sleep."

"I'll massage it for you."

I took my shoe off and leant against the car while he did so. His touch sent tingles up my spine.

"Better now?" he asked after a few minutes.

"Mm." I hobbled into an upright position and clutched his arm while I replaced my shoe. We were in a multi-storey car park which was quite dark and when we reached the street, the bright lights made me blink.

"Hungry? Fancy some fish and chips? There's a 'Chippy' over there."

"Lovely."

We ate our meal out of the paper as we walked and talked. Then we went back to the car and he put his arms round me and kissed me. I got goose pimples again. He was so lovely. I wished the evening would never end. But of course it had to. He brought his arm round my neck to look at his watch.

"It's nearly midnight. I'd better get you back, Cinderella."

"Oh dear," I sighed. "I wish I didn't have to go back."

"So do I," he said kissing me again. "I'm afraid you'll have to get in the back again."

I managed to get back to the car park without being seen and hoped my hair wasn't in too much of a mess. I'd lost the foam lining that supported my headscarf so I looked very different from the way I'd looked at the Meeting. I was heading for the 'Ladies' to do a repair job when Tony Bates grabbed my arm. He looked furious.

"I've been looking for you, Sarah. Where have you been?"

My heart started to pound and I hoped he couldn't hear it. "I was talking to people and then I went to the 'Ladies'," I said nonchalantly.

"Well come along now. Mrs Bates is waiting."

He frogmarched me off like a naughty child and I remembered I'd never got to the loo. I hoped I wouldn't disgrace myself on the way home. Fortunately I didn't but I'd obviously blotted my copy book yet again as I wasn't invited to a Bristol Meeting again for a very long time. Peter and I had to find other ways to meet.

CHAPTER FIVE

⌘

TWO BURIALS AND A VOW

Even though I walk through the Valley
of the shadow of death, I will fear no evil,
for you are with me. [Psalm 23:4]

The rest of the summer went really quickly and
it seemed no time at all that I was back at school. I
hadn't seen my grandfather for some time and I was
feeling guilty about him but it was so difficult to shake
Ruth off. She was still acting as my shadow.

Just before we broke up for the Christmas holidays,
Tony Bates' mother died. Mrs Piper was a sweet old
lady and I'd sometimes visited her as she lived with the
Bates. But she'd become ill and had quickly gone
downhill. I was sorry she'd died and I knew we'd have
to go to the burial. I hated burials. We all had to go,
even the very young children – I always got the giggles
although it was such a very solemn occasion.

The burial was on Wednesday and Ruth and I signed out of school at lunchtime as the burial was at one o'clock. I was glad Katie was away from school and wouldn't be able to go because I knew she'd make me laugh even more.

I changed my blouse for a black jumper and tied my navy headscarf over my head. Mum, Dad, Rachel, Richard and I all piled into the car. Tim, my other brother, wasn't coming. He was a rebel like me and he'd refused to go. I wished I'd been able to but it would have been too much hassle.

When we reached the Meeting Room, everyone looked even more solemn than usual and I immediately wanted to giggle. I gritted my teeth together and looked down at my feet. I should have cleaned my shoes. They were dusty.

I followed Mum into the Room and we climbed up to the back row. I started to feel sick as the open coffin was carried in by Tony Bates and other brothers. They set it down in the middle of the floor and I tried not to look. But I knew I would have to. My eyes were drawn to the wrinkled white face surrounded by wispy strands of hair. My lips twitched. I knew it wasn't at all funny but the solemnity always had that effect on me. I shut my eyes and put my hand firmly over my mouth.

The Meeting droned on and the singing was even worse than usual. It lasted for about an hour but at last it was over. The coffin lid was replaced, the coffin lifted up and we filed out in silence behind it. We drove to the cemetery beside the Parish Church. I was surprised we didn't have a burial ground of our own. Fancy being buried beside Anglicans!

We followed the coffin to the newly dug grave and I knew the worst part was about to happen. We sang a hymn and my breath froze; it was so cold. Tony Bates prayed and then some of the young brothers started to throw earth down on the coffin lid. I felt really sick and I was very glad to get back in the car. I was shivering and not only with the cold.

Depression engulfed me when I got home. I didn't even want to go to work at the Hawes. Mum and Dad were at home so I couldn't phone without them hearing.

"I'm just going for a walk," I called.

I pulled on a coat and ran out of the house round the corner to a phone box to phone Janice – as I'd been told to call her.

"Do you mind if I don't come today?" I asked. "I've just been to a burial and it was awful. I feel so depressed."

"Wouldn't it cheer you up to see the children?"

"I don't think it would."

"All right, dear. I'll see you tomorrow."

I put the phone down and trailed back to the house. My life stretched before me in an empty nothingness. What was there to look forward to?

I'd decided I would definitely go to see my grandfather the day we broke up but I couldn't get rid of Ruth. Then Mum wanted me to cook the dinner when

I got home so I couldn't go out again. I was determined to see him some time before we went back to school.

Then one day Dad came in looking very solemn. I was just crossing the hall and looked at him in surprise.

"What's the matter, Dad?"

"Find your mother and the others and come into the lounge. I want to talk to you."

Mum appeared and I called Rachel but Richard and Tim were out.

"What's the matter, John?" asked Mum as we sat down.

Dad didn't reply for a moment. When he did, his voice sounded odd – as though he was trying not to cry.

"I've had some bad news. My – my father has been killed in a road accident. He....."

"Oh no!" I screamed. "No. He can't have. I was going to see him. I must see him. I......."

"Be quiet, Sarah," said Mum firmly. "Let your father finish."

But I couldn't stop crying. I sobbed and sobbed. Why hadn't I made more of an effort to see him again? I hardly heard what Dad was saying.

"It was his fault. He drove straight out of side turning into a lorry. He never stood a chance."

"I'm so sorry, dear," said Mum softly. "I know we – we didn't agree with him but – but he was still your father."

"Yes." Dad stood up abruptly and walked out.

Rachel had started crying and soon Mum joined in as well. But they couldn't have felt as sad as I did. They didn't know him like I did. How I wished I'd defied Dad and gone to see him in spite of the rules. What a coward I'd been. I'd never forgive myself.

"Where's Grandad's funeral, Dad?" I asked the next day as I pushed my dinner round my plate. I didn't think I'd ever feel hungry again.

"I expect it'll be in the Chapel where he worshipped."

"Do you know when it is?"

"Er – no."

I didn't believe him. "Dad, you do know, don't you?"

"I think it's Friday."

"Can we go?"

"Of course not."

"I think we should. He was your Dad. I want to go."

"Sarah, you know perfectly well we can't go. The Brethren would never allow it."

"We don't have to tell them."

"Sarah!" Mum was horrified.

"Well we don't," I said sulkily. "I shall go."

"You are not to, Sarah. Do you hear?"

I wasn't going to listen. I knew where the Chapel was and I was determined to go. But then I had second thoughts. I'd never been to a service anywhere but the

Meeting. I'd feel very odd. But perhaps I could go to the graveside. I was sure he'd be buried in the same churchyard as Mrs Piper. I knew I wouldn't laugh at this burial. Dad had been thinking along the same lines. At dinner the following night he said, "Tony Bates has refused to allow us to go to the Chapel service but he says we can go to the graveside – as long as we don't stand near the other mourners."

I made a disgusted sound and Dad glared at me. I certainly wasn't going to 'stand apart'.

On Friday I spent much of the morning praying and asking God to forgive me for not going to see my grandfather. I still felt so awful about it. It was so hard to accept that I'd never see him again.

We drove in silence to the cemetery and waited in the road until the coffin and the other mourners arrived. There were a lot of them. All the women wore hats and I felt very conspicuous in my stupid headscarf. I was sorry Aunt Jenny couldn't be there and I wondered if I'd discover any other relatives.

When the others were grouped round the grave, we walked towards them and stopped about twelve feet away. I felt really stupid. I glanced at Mum and Dad. Then I moved forward. I daren't join the rest of the party but at least I'd made a move towards them. A girl, in her twenties, wearing a black pill box hat with a veil, glanced across at me and smiled. Tentatively I smiled back.

The singing was lovely – much better than the Brethren but I didn't know the hymn so I couldn't join in. The Brethren had their own hymn book and had long ago discarded most of the familiar 'church' hymns.

The singing finished and one of the men stepped forward. I wondered if he was a relative. His words were very moving. He thanked God for Grandad's life and spoke about the break up of his family. Tears started to fall down my cheeks and I dropped my head as the speaker asked God to unite our family again.

Then it was over and I watched the mourners move closer to the grave before the earth was thrown in. I wanted to join them but knew it would be asking for trouble.

"Sarah." Mum came forward and touched my arm. "We're going now. Come along."

"I'll come in a minute. I want to stay quietly for a little while."

I knew she didn't want me to but she wouldn't make a scene. The footsteps receded on the gravel path and I was left with the other mourners. Suddenly I felt awkward. Should I go to speak to them? Or would they turn their backs on me? A lump formed in my throat and tears started to cascade down my cheeks. Once started I couldn't stop. I sobbed and sobbed. Grief for all the lost years overwhelmed me and my heart felt as though it had been sliced clean through by a sharp knife.

Suddenly I felt an arm round my shoulders.

"Don't cry, Sarah. He wouldn't have wanted you to cry so much."

"I never said goodbye to him," I sobbed. "Oh, why did I let them pressure me into not seeing him? I feel so guilty."

"You were the most important thing in his life. Finding you again made his life worth living."

"Really?" I peered through my tears. The girl in the pill box hat still had her arms round me. "How do you know?"

"He told me so. I'm Tessa, your cousin. Come and meet my parents."

Still sobbing, I let her lead me. I seemed to have no will of my own. Through a haze I was aware of being comforted by my new found relatives, Uncle Adrian and Aunt Rosemary. I couldn't stop crying and nothing they said removed my tremendous guilt and heart-break.

At last I had to go because I knew Mum and Dad were waiting for me in the car. At the end of my black tunnel a tiny pin prick of light had appeared. I had found my relatives and I didn't want to lose touch with them again. Tessa had given me her phone number and I hoped I'd somehow manage to meet her.

The following Tuesday we went back to school. I was just hanging up my coat when Bridget came by.

"Oh, I've got something for you," she said. "It's a Christmas card from your grandfather. He was so sorry he didn't see you before Christmas to give it to you himself. He waited every day by the gate but you didn't go past. He knew I went to the same school, so he asked me to give it to you. Why Sarah, whatever's the matter?"

"He was killed," I sobbed. "In a road accident – just before Christmas. And I meant to go to see him. Now I'll never be able to."

Bridget put her arms round me as I sobbed and sobbed.

"Hush, hush," she whispered. "Your grandfather wouldn't want you to grieve like this. He'd understand. And he's happy now, with the Lord Jesus, isn't he?"

"Yes, of course but it does hurt so, Bridget."

"I know." She thrust some tissues at me. "I didn't know about the accident or I might not have given you the card. I'm so sorry. Do you want to go home? I can tell Mrs Lane you're not very well."

"No." I blew my nose vigorously. "No, I'll be all right. I'm sorry, Bridget."

"Don't be silly. There's nothing to be sorry for. Sure you're all right now?"

I nodded and put the card in my bag. All day I was miserable and tears kept threatening but I managed to keep them at bay. I couldn't wait to get home so I could look at the card and indulge in the luxury of a good weep where no one would see me. At last school finished and I ran home so fast my 'shadow' couldn't keep up with me. I flung myself into my room and locked the door. My hands were shaking so much I could hardly open the envelope. On the front of the card was a picture of a dove holding an olive branch in its beak. Inside Grandad had written:

```
To my dear granddaughter, Sarah,
        You are like a ray of sunshine in m
life. All your loving kindness to me
has been been much appreciated.
                Your loving,
                Grandfather
```

I threw myself on my bed and cried and cried. How could I have been so cruel? I was aware of nothing except a thick black fog of pain and hopelessness all round me. It must have been hours later when I heard Rachel calling me from downstairs.

"Sarah. Mum says it's dinner time."

Still sobbing, I rolled off the bed and opened the door. "I don't want anything to eat. I don't feel very well. I'm going to bed."

It was true. I felt sick from crying. I changed into my nightdress and got into bed. When Mum came up, I pretended to be asleep and she went away without disturbing me. I lay in the dark, thinking. Nothing I could do would bring Grandad back but perhaps I could do something for him that would make me feel less guilty.

The next day after school, I managed to get rid of Ruth and I returned to Grandad's grave. The tears welled up again. I'd cried so much I felt really ill. Sobs racked my body as I stooped down and touched the earth above my grandfather. I thought I was alone and no one would see my grief so I was startled when someone touched me gently and I heard a concerned voice say, "Can I help you, dear?"

I looked up into the troubled eyes of an elderly lady. Her kindness only made me sob more and she put her arms round me as I gave vent to my sorrow against her shoulder. She didn't seem to mind. At last I drew away, scrabbling for a tissue in my pocket.

"I'm sorry," I muttered.

"Don't worry, dear. It's good to let the grief come out. Do you want to talk about it?"

"My grandfather died and I never said, 'goodbye' to him." I couldn't tell her all the details. I still felt loyalty to my family.

"I'm sure he would have understood. You mustn't torture yourself, dear."

I sniffed and blew my nose. "I'm all right now. Thank you for coming over."

"I was putting some flowers on my husband's grave. He died last year. I still miss him."

"I'm so sorry."

"Thank you. Are you sure you're all right now?"

I nodded and she returned to tend her husband's grave. After she'd gone, I stared down at the grave thinking about Grandad and praying for God's blessing on our broken family.

Then I made a vow. "Oh God," I prayed aloud. "I vow before you that with your help I will bring together the three children of my dear grandfather – John, Jenny and Adrian. I pray that they will again be one united family in you. Amen."

Tears were streaming down my face as I finished but I didn't care. If I could fulfil my vow, perhaps I could blot out the guilt I still felt at not seeing my grandfather again before he died.

CHAPTER SIX

✼

THE 'WORLD' ISN'T SO BAD!

'I am troubled; O Lord, come to my aid!'
[Isaiah 38:14]

I was fifteen the following April. There was still another year before I could leave school and I was getting fed up with it. There was so much course work to do for G.C.S.E. and I found it difficult to concentrate. I was still working for the Hawes and I'd had to let Mum into the secret. One evening towards the end of the summer term, I had a lovely surprise. I'd just finished giving Edward and Caroline their tea when Janice came in and handed me a letter.

"I think it's from your Aunt Jenny," she said.

I looked at the New Zealand postmark and grinned. "That's marvellous."

Janice smiled. "Do you want to read it now? I'll take the children into the other room."

"If you don't mind. Thanks."

I tore open the envelope and a number of flimsy air mail sheets fell out; I was soon giggling over Aunt Jenny's account of her life in New Zealand. She made it sound such fun. I couldn't wait to go there.

But the most exciting news came at the end. "Your Uncle Adrian's going to renovate your grandfather's house and the family's going to live in it," she wrote.

"Yippee!" I shouted and Janice rushed in to see if I was all right. I waved the letter at her. "My Uncle Adrian's family is going to move into my grandad's house. Imagine having them that close. It'll be lovely to have my cousins so near. I do hope I can see them. I'll have to plan it carefully."

"It may be some time yet," Janice warned. "The house needs a lot doing to it."

"Does it?" I'd never been inside, of course, and I hadn't really looked at it properly. "Still it will certainly be something to look forward to."

I couldn't wait to get home to write back. I also wrote to Tessa who had a house of her own in Kent. She was several years older than I was. Rachel came in before I'd finished and I hastily thrust both letters under the bed.

"What are you doing?" she asked suspiciously. Although she was my best friend, I didn't feel I could share this secret with anyone.

"Nothing," I answered airily going out of the room. Of course Rachel decided to tidy up and she found the letters and read them. I was furious when I found out.

"You've no right to read other people's letters," I stormed. "Don't you dare tell anyone."

She looked smug. "I might and then again, I might not."

I threw a pillow at her. "You'd better not."

I didn't think she would but I wasn't sure. Fortunately there were no repercussions so I assumed she hadn't mentioned it. It was dreadful not having any privacy. I posted the letters the next day and hoped I'd hear from Tessa soon but it was ages before she wrote and I gave up waiting for her letter. I had other things to think about.

Towards the end of the summer term everyone was talking about the places they were going to visit during the holidays. I felt an 'outsider' as we weren't allowed to go away at all – not even to the seaside for a day. I was desperate to see more of the world and it was difficult even to travel a few miles without getting into trouble. I hated being stuck at home and only going out to boring Meetings. I felt depressed, too, that I seemed no nearer fulfilling my vow. I hadn't heard from Tessa or met any of my relatives again. I wondered when her family would move into Grandad's house.

When we returned to school, everyone was talking about the marvellous time they'd had. Fortunately, no one listened to anyone else's saga, so I escaped being singled out as an 'oddball'.

Ruth continued to 'shadow' me but I'd devised ways to avoid her so I had a little more privacy. It was after the Christmas holidays when I suddenly realised how quickly the time was passing and how much work I still had to do before the G.C.S.E. exams.

I had a project to do for Childcare that should have been done weeks before and if I didn't hand it in soon, I wouldn't be entered for the exam. and I didn't want that. I was relieved when it was finally completed and I took it to Mrs White.

"What are you going to do when you leave, Sarah?" she asked. "You should start to think about it, you know."

"I'd like to be a nanny," I blurted out. But I knew I couldn't. I wouldn't be allowed to look after the children of 'worldlies'.

Mrs White looked interested. "I think you'd make a good one, Sarah. You like small children, don't you?"

"Yes. I do. But—but I don't think my parents would let me."

She looked puzzled. "Why not?"

I thought fast. "I think they've got other plans for me," I said hurriedly. They had! I'd have to be a boring secretary for some pompous brother and then I'd be married off! Ugh!

"Well if you change your mind, let me know."

"I will."

I left her, feeling miserable. I didn't want to work for the Brethren. I wanted to try something different 'outside' - in the 'world'.

My heart lurched. Would I really be brave enough to work for 'worldlies'? I sighed as I trailed in – late as usual – to the English lesson.

The mock exams were looming and I hadn't done enough work. I usually managed to get by but I knew I'd have to revise for the real thing. Part of me wanted to do really well but then I wondered why I should bother. I couldn't have a proper career like the rest of my classmates. I felt very depressed about it.

I didn't do too badly in the mock exams. In fact I came top in English Literature with seventy four! The average mark was forty! I celebrated by cycling into town at lunch time – without my headscarf. I bought some chips and a couple of magazines.

In the afternoon we had Geography and I was bored so I read a magazine under the desk. Unfortunately Mr Brown saw and went mad at me. He took it away and promptly read it himself! After the lesson he kept me behind and threatened to write to Mum and Dad because he said I was always talking and not concentrating. I put on my most innocent expression and promised to work harder so he said he wouldn't write 'for the moment'.

Of course I'd been seen cycling into the town. On Sunday after the 'Supper', Tony Bates cornered me.

"You were seen last week without a headscarf, Sarah," he said pompously.

I couldn't think what he was talking about and told him so. He bristled.

"There's no need to be rude, Sarah," he reproved me. "You were cycling in the High Street on Wednesday – without a headscarf."

I might have known his spies were everywhere. "I can't wear a headscarf when I'm cycling," I informed him. "It falls off."

"Then you should fasten it more securely."

"It doesn't make any difference. Sorry, I've got to go. Mum's calling me." I knew I'd told him a lie but I hated wearing a headscarf. I felt such a lemon. I never wore one when I was cycling.

The term rushed by and I spent the Easter holidays trying to revise but I wasn't very organised. I'd only got one more term. I'd been applying for secretarial jobs because I was determined I wasn't going to work for any Brethren; but I couldn't go on to further training as we had to leave school at sixteen so there weren't many opportunities.

When we went back for the Summer term, the exams. started almost immediately. I asked Jesus to help me. In spite of the rules and regulations we were bound by, I always thought of him as my friend and I talked to him when I had problems. I knew he understood everything about me.

A really weird thing happened during the Childcare exam. When I turned over the paper, I looked at the questions and was sure I couldn't answer any of them. I said a quick prayer and started writing a sentence.

Then I found myself writing things I didn't even know I knew. It was very peculiar – the most odd thing that had ever happened to me and I knew it was because Jesus had been guiding me.

The next day I had a letter from St Mark's hospital saying I'd been short listed for a clerical officer post. Then after school there was a phone call from the Alfred Marks Bureau saying a computor firm in the town wanted me to work for them as an office junior. They wanted me to start the following week! Life suddenly felt very exciting.

I phoned to explain I was still taking my exams. and wouldn't be able to start work for several weeks. They said they'd let me know if the firm was still interested.

I was too restless to revise and the Business Studies exam. the next day was a disaster. There were questions on everything I hadn't revised and nothing I had. I managed to write something and I was in full flow when I ran out of paper and put my hand up for more.

Miss Bryce came over and hissed that she'd had to send over to the main block for some more so I'd have to wait. I was mad. It seemed ages before I was finally given some. She was very apologetic but it was still very unfair. I was half way down the new sheet when all the lights went out! There was a power cut! At least we were given some extra time when they finally came on again. The hall only had windows on one side so we needed lights.

The next day I got up at six and went into school early to practise my typing. But I didn't do much because Katie was there and we talked all the time instead. The typing exam. was better than the Business Studies one.

The others weren't too bad and I ate sweets all the time to keep up my strength. Then at last it was my final day at school. I wasn't too sad to be leaving. I was just glad to finish my exams.

My darling Peter phoned in the evening and we had a long chat. It was ages since I'd seen him. He was such a good friend and I could talk properly to him.

I celebrated leaving school by reading most of the night! I had a few hours' sleep and the next day it was sunny and hot so I took a chair and a book and went outside to sunbathe. I felt so sorry for all those poor things still in classes. The school didn't break up for another month.

It was so peaceful and I lay back and shut my eyes. It was wonderful not to have to revise. I was nearly asleep when I felt it grow dark.

"Bother," I thought. Was the sun going to disappear for the rest of the day?

I opened my eyes to inspect the sky and at the same time I nearly choked. The darkness wasn't from clouds. Billows of smoke were drifting over the fence from our neighbour's bonfire! I was so mad and I'd got black specks all over me.

"Bother, bother, bother," I shouted crossly as I grabbed my things and ran inside.

I lazed around for the rest of the day and the following day I had an interview at St Mark's Hospital. It was very informal. I was shown round while they talked to me and asked me questions. Then they offered me the job of medical secretary. It sounded interesting but I had other options so I said I'd let them know.

In the afternoon Alfred Marks phoned to ask if I was still interested in working for the computor firm in the town. I decided to say I was and they said I could start the following day. I didn't even have an interview!

Mum and Dad weren't pleased.

"Why do you always have to be different, Sarah?" sighed Mum.

"You know Brian Forbes has offered you a job in his building firm," said Dad. "Why won't you take that?"

I gritted my teeth. "I'm sorry," I said firmly. "I just don't want to work for Brian Forbes or any other Brethren. Why can't you understand?"

"But the Brethren don't approve of you working for someone in 'the world'. They'll be really angry."

"I don't care," I screamed. "I can't believe the Brethren are the only Christians although they behave as if they are." I rushed up to my room. I wished I didn't have to grow up. Life was going to get really complicated I was sure.

That night I was really sick. I thought I was dying. Mum dosed me with milk of magnesia but I was up and down to the loo all night so I hardly got any sleep. I suppose I was nervous about working for 'worldlies'. Would they all really be as 'bad' as the Brethren said they were? Perhaps I'd made a mistake.

I felt better the next morning and cycled to the town. The firm was quite large and I found it a bit nerve racking meeting all the top salesmen and managers. But they were all very kind to me and one of the secretaries, Linda, took me under her wing.

"This is your desk. I'm afraid there's not much room. We're a bit squashed. Have you used a word processor before?" Should I admit I hadn't? I decided to be honest and she looked surprised. "I thought you used them at school."

I was embarrassed. How could I tell her that I belonged to an odd group that refused to have anything to do with computers? Fortunately she didn't pursue it. She gave me a brief lesson and by the end of the day I was quite proficient on the machine. I was very pleased with myself. I also did a lot of photocopying and took a number of phone messages. By the end of the day I was quite tired but relieved I'd survived my first day in 'the world'. The others who worked in the same room were friendly and I looked forward to my next day.

By the end of the week I felt as though I'd been there years and had heard all the gossip about the bosses and the secretaries. They were all very pleasant ordinary people—not 'wicked' at all! There wasn't really enough work for me so I started to get a bit bored.

I cheered up the next week when Bill Hawes, Janice's husband, came into the room where I was struggling with the telex machine which had broken down on me.

"Hi, Sarah. They said I could come through. I've got a letter for you."

"A letter?"

"You gave your cousin our address, didn't you?"

"Oh yes." I'd almost forgotten about Tessa. I'd written to her so long ago.

"I was passing so I thought you'd like it straight away. It came this morning."

"Thanks. I really appreciate it. Would you like a coffee? The telex machine is on the blink. I think it needs a rest. So do I."

He laughed. "I'd love one."

There was no one else in the room so we chatted briefly over a very welcome cup of coffee and then he left. I glared at the offending machine and decided it could do with a longer rest while I read my letter. I was glad there was no one around. It was nearly lunch time so I decided to eat my sanwiches. The others would be going to the pub. They'd invited me but I wasn't yet ready to break all the Brethren's rules. I was also terrified at the thought of going to a pub. I wouldn't know how to behave.

The letter was a long one and I learnt a lot about my 'new' cousin. She sounded really nice. Her house sounded wonderful. How I wished I could have a house of my own. Even a bedroom to myself would be an improvement.

Tessa said she'd got a boy friend and she sympathised with the difficulty I had in meeting Peter. "It's so crazy to expect young people to find a partner when they put so much strain on relationships," she wrote. "This religious thing worries me as it does you. Don't let them blind you to the truth which I think, thankfully, you can see. Yes, God is much more interested in the important things in life than the trivial matters the Brethren seem to be so wrapped up with. It is far more important to show you care for people."

She went on to tell me about her church which was 'Evangelical'. She said some of the members had once been members of the Brethren. Tears started to fall when I got to the end and I was so glad I was alone. "It is so sad when this religious thing messes up friendships. It never should. God wants us to love one another, to settle our differences and live happily together. His Church was never meant to get in between people."

Then she said she'd always be ready to listen if I wanted to talk and perhaps we could meet sometime. Some of my tears had fallen on the page and I blotted them with a tissue. I could hear the others returning from lunch so I hurriedly dried my eyes and returned to my battle with the telex machine. It worked! It *had* needed a rest.

The following week Linda rushed in bursting with news.

"Terry and Tracy are getting married!" she exclaimed.

Terry was one of the bosses and he'd been living with his secretary, Tracy, for ages. I was pleased they were getting married at last and joined in the general congratulations when Tracy came in. She looked radiant and I was briefly jealous.

That feeling vanished when she said happily, "You'll all come to the wedding, won't you? It's not going to be a big affair. We're only going to have the family at the Reception but you're all invited to St Bridget's church at two thirty on Saturday 20th August."

There was a general hubbub as she left and I hoped no one would notice my lack of enthusiasm. Linda came across to me.

"Isn't that great? We can go together. What will you wear?"

I turned away so she couldn't see my face. Jesus went to a wedding. In fact he performed a miracle there when he turned the water into wine. He must have enjoyed himself with all his friends around him. But of course I couldn't go to Tracy's wedding. The Brethren would have a fit if they heard I'd been into a Church! We weren't allowed to go anywhere but the Meeting. I tried frantically to think of an excuse. I couldn't tell her the truth.

"I'd love to go but I've already arranged to go out with my parents on that day."

Even to my ears it sounded pretty feeble but she accepted it.

"What a shame. I'll have to tell you all about it."

"Oh yes please." I must have sounded too enthusiastic as she gave me a very odd look as she walked back to her desk.

I was really fed up on the Saturday of the wedding. I kept imagining what it was like. I was sure it would be a lovely occasion.

During the Break on Sunday I was standing near Mrs Bates and I heard her say to Rachel, "It must be so hard for you, dear, having a sister like Sarah. I feel so sorry for your family."

She could have been a bit more tactful. Rachel looked embarrassed and I glared at her. I wished I had gone to Tracy's wedding. I was the black sheep already so a little more black ink wouldn't make much difference.

In the evening I cycled to the Meeting – without a headscarf again, to show my independence. I could see everyone was horrified as I rode into the car park but I didn't care. Of course I put it on before I went into the Meeting. No one said anything that time. They'd probably decided I was past redemption.

On Monday the whole office was talking of nothing but the wedding and I felt left out.

"What a pity you couldn't go, Sarah," said Linda. "Did you have a nice day out?"

"What? Oh yes – thanks." I'd forgotten the feeble esxcuse I'd given. I hoped she wouldn't ask me for any details or I'd have to lie again. Fortunately she didn't.

The exam. results were due the following Friday. On Thursday night I dreamt I'd failed them all! The postman came just as I was leaving for work. I rushed over to him.

"Have you got my exam. results?" I gasped.

"Dunno love." He handed me a couple of envelopes but they were both bills. "Sorry. They'll probably come next post."

I couldn't concentrate all day and when I got home, there was the brown envelope on the hall table waiting for me. My heart started beating and my hands were shaking so much I could hardly pick it up. When I did, I rushed to the bathroom and locked the door. Then I sat on the loo and stared at the envelope. I was too terrified to open it. Eventually I forced myself and tore it open snatching out the flimsy paper. I couldn't believe it! I'd got three As, five Bs and one C. I was thrilled particularly as I hadn't done much revision. I'd even beaten Tim. He'd only got eight O Levels. I'd got nine G.C.S.E.s!

On Monday I plucked up courage to go to the hairdresser after work for the first time. Rachel had had another go at my hair and once again she'd made a mess of it. She had to cut way above my shoulder to get it straight. It was so short, I knew I'd be in trouble again. Linda had kept telling me to go to the hairdresser as it looked so awful. I was really nervous in case he made it too noticeable but luckily he did as I asked and just trimmed it. I felt really 'wicked' sitting in the chair as he worked on my hair. What would Tony Bates say?

The next day at work everyone said how pretty it looked so I was glad I'd had it done. I was getting a bit fed up with work as there wasn't much to do and I was getting bored. I was also bothered by the pressure Linda and the others kept putting on me to go out to the pub for lunch. Every day Linda pleaded with me.

"Come on, Sarah. It's fun and you don't have to drink alcohol. You can have a fruit juice."

"I'd rather not," I said for the hundredth time. "I'm quite happy eating my sandwiches here."

"Bring them with you."

"Linda, I really don't want to go!" I exclaimed. "Please don't keep asking me."

How could I explain to her it wasn't the alcohol that was the problem; after all our ex-leader, now deceased, had instructed the Brethren to have whisky on their tables 'to demonstrate liberty' whatever that meant. No, I wasn't a teetotaller; it was mixing socially with 'worldlies' that was the trouble. A pub must be a terrible place, I thought. And although my colleagues were pleasant, I hadn't yet found any Christians among them.

Eventually Linda went off in a huff and I sat and thought. Perhaps I should change jobs. I eyed the phone speculatively and then rummaged in my handbag for my diary. I found the phone number of the Alfred Marks Employment Agency.

Apprehensively, I dialled. "It's Sarah Foster here," I said when the phone was answered. "You found me a job when I left school but I'm not really being stretched enough and I just wondered if you had anything else."

"Just a minute. I'll get your file."

She was gone ages and I hoped the others wouldn't return from the pub too quickly.

"We could offer you a job here. You'd be a filing clerk and do some word processing. You've been doing that, haven't you?"

"Yes." I felt excited. Perhaps things were going to work out for me.

"You'll have to give a week's notice. Could you start Monday week?"

"That would be great. Thanks."

I couldn't believe it. But I was a bit worried about having to tell my present boss. To my surprise he was quite pleasant about it and so was Linda.

"You haven't really been happy here, have you, Sarah?" she asked shrewdly.

I blushed. "You've all been very nice to me," I told her.

"You'll have to come to the pub on your last day. I'll buy you a drink."

I worried about that while I worked out my notice but I didn't see how I could avoid making my debut in a notorious Public House! I didn't tell Mum and Dad!

They'd have been horrified. Although I wanted to leave, when my last day came, I felt sad.

"We'll miss you," said Tracy when she brought in some papers for me to photocopy.

"Yes we will." There was a chorus from the other girls and, to my annoyance, I started to cry.

"I'll miss you, too," I sobbed, grabbing a handful of tissues from the box on the desk.

Linda put her arm round me and that made me feel worse! I still felt awful when we left to go to 'The Waggoners' Walk'. It was only a few minutes' walk from the office and I kept glancing behind me to make sure no one was spying on me. I had to force my feet over the threshold. I was so scared. I thought God might strike me dead for going into such a wicked place.

There was loud music blaring out as Linda shepherded me to an empty table.

"What'll you have?"

I thought quickly. "A sherry please."

That seemed safe. We had sherry in the house and I sometimes drank a little when I couldn't sleep. Linda looked surprised as she went off to buy it. She'd obviously expected me to ask for a fruit juice.

I looked round. Several men were propping up the bar, a couple of girls were giggling at the next table and an elderly couple opposite were eating fish and chips. I started to relax. It wasn't as bad as I'd expected.

"Here you are." Linda dumped a glass in front of me. "It's medium. Hope that's all right. I forgot to ask you what sort."

I took a sip. It tasted different from the one we had at home but it was pleasant.

"Cheers." Linda raised her glass. "Here's to your new job."

"Thanks." I gulped some sherry, feeling sad. I would miss Linda.

"We'll have to meet some time and you can tell me all about it. I haven't got your phone number. Let me have it and I'll call you."

"I – er – I – ." What was I to do? She couldn't ring me at home. "Give me your number and I'll phone you," I said quickly.

"Promise?"

"Promise."

I was still sad when the end of the day came and I had to say goodbye to everyone. They were all so kind and I felt embarrassed.

The new job was more demanding but I soon settled in. To my delight I soon found there were a number of Christians working in the same office. One girl, Eileen, worked at the next desk and a few days after I'd started, she said to me. "Do you go to Church, Sarah?"

I was so startled I dropped my pen and bending down to pick it up gave me a little time to think of a suitable answer.

"Well it's not exactly a Church," I said. "It's - er – just a small group of Christians meeting together." What else could I say? "Where do you go?"

"I go to the New Wine Fellowship. It's really lively. Perhaps you'd like to come with me one Sunday."

"I'd love to," I heard myself say. What was I thinking of? Of course I couldn't go – could I?

She didn't say any more but over the next few weeks I thought about it. I was trying to remember why the New Wine Fellowship sounded so familiar. I knew I'd heard of it before but I couldn't think where.

Then one night just before Christmas it came to me. I was almost asleep and I shot up in bed, exclaiming, "Of course, Bridget and Miss Jones!"

"What? What's the matter? Sarah, are you all right?" Rachel sounded scared. I'd woken her up. Bother, I thought.

"Sorry, Rachel. I just thought of something. That's all."

"Well there's no need to shout about it," said my sister crossly. "Was it important?"

"Yes. I think it might be," I said thoughtfully lying back again. I remembered the R.E. lesson I'd gone to by mistake and how Bridget had shared her Bible with me. She'd told me afterwards she went to the same Church as Miss Jones, the New Wine Fellowship. Fancy calling it a 'fellowship'. I'd thought that word was only used by the Brethren. Yes I would go one day. It was beginning to feel as if it was meant. Perhaps God did have a plan for my life. It would be interesting to see what other Christian services were like. But the opportunity didn't come for several weeks.

Meanwhile Christmas was nearly upon us and I was worried because I'd be expected to go to the Christmas party and I was afraid to. There was no one I could talk to about my fears – only Jesus – and sometimes he seemed so far away. I wrote all my feelings down in my diary; that helped to keep me sane. It was awful having to keep everything bottled up.

Eileen was very kind and often talked about her Church but I was glad she didn't ask me again about mine. I wasn't yet ready to tell her about it. It seemed disloyal.

Then a few days before Christmas one of the other girls came over to us. "Can I have ten pounds for the Christmas 'do', please? We're going to Barnaby's and they'll do a special price for us."

Eileen got out her purse but my stomach lurched. Laura turned to me.

"Sarah?"

I opened my mouth but couldn't say anything. Eileen came to my rescue.

"We all go out for dinner just before Christmas," she explained. "You don't have to come, Sarah."

"But everyone goes," exclaimed Laura.

"I'm afraid I haven't got ten pounds on me at the moment," I said. "I'll give it to you later." Coward, I thought. You know you're afraid to go.

"O.K." Laura left and Eileen looked at me.

"What's the matter, Sarah?" Her kindness was the last straw and tears started to pour down my cheeks. I was glad no one else was around. "You don't have to tell me if you'd rather not. But it might help to talk, you know."

I took a deep breath and suddenly the wall I'd built between me and 'the world' collapsed and I started to talk. I told her about the Brethren and my frustration and how wicked I was. She just listened, without interrupting once.

"Sometimes I feel so lonely," I ended. "The Brethren don't accept me and I don't really belong in the – 'world' either. I'm sort of in limbo."

"Poor Sarah," said Eileen. "I guessed that you belonged to the Brethren but I wasn't sure. It's the very strict group, isn't it?"

I nodded. "I want to leave but I don't know what to do."

"When you want to talk, don't forget I'm here."

"Thank you. It's such a relief. I haven't been able to talk to anyone before."

I forgot about the Christmas dinner but a few days later, Eileen asked me if I was going.

"I've never been to a restaurant before," I said shyly. "We're told they're such evil places."

She laughed. "All we do is eat a meal together."

"That's what's wrong," I said quickly. "We're not allowed to eat meals with 'worldlies'. Oh dear!" I clapped my hand over my mouth in embarrassemnt but to my relief, she laughed again. In fact she kept on laughing.

"I'm sorry," she said at last, wiping her eyes. "But I've never been called a 'worldly' before. Some people in my Church also disapprove of 'worldlies' but they mean people who don't have any morals and really do bad things."

"Oh." I hadn't realised other Christians might also have reservations about 'the world'. I thought about the dinner and made up my mind. "I'll come to the dinner," I said. "Then I can make up my own mind, can't I?"

The day of the dinner turned into one long party. Drinks were brought in at lunch time and all afternoon we did nothing but eat and drink. I decided I loved parties. In the evening I had to eat dinner at home before I left for the office outing or Mum would have been suspicious. I told her I had to go back to the office to finish off some work because of the Christmas rush.

When I got back to the office, Eileen drove me to Barnaby's – a very posh restaurant. There were red cloths and candles on all the tables. It all looked very Christmassy and once again I was sorry we didn't keep Christmas. Eileen and I pulled our crackers and put on paper hats. I felt rather awkward. It was the first time I'd been in a restaurant and I wasn't sure what to order or what knives to use. And I certainly couldn't join in with the conversation. Apart from Eileen, I had little in common with any of my workmates. Fortunately

Eileen helped me but I felt very apprehensive most of the time although the champagne and other wine helped me to relax a little. By the end of the evening I didn't feel too good. I'd been eating and drinking for about eleven hours! One of the men drove me home and, of course, Mum and Dad were still up waiting for me.

"Where have you been, Sarah?" stormed Mum. "We've been so worried."

"I – I've been with my friends," I giggled trying to stand upright and focus my eyes on Mum. There seemed to be two of her.

"Have you been drinking, Sarah?" demanded Dad.

"Only – very – leetle. Feel happy." I clutched the bannisters to stop myself falling over.

"You're a very wicked girl. Why did you lie to us? You said you were working late."

I shook my head but it hurt so I stopped. "Not working. Eating. Eating with 'worldlies'." I giggled again.

"Go to bed, Sarah," sighed Mum. "We'll talk in the morning when you're sober."

"Am – sh – shober." I collapsed on the stairs and started to crawl up them. After I'd splashed cold water all over my face, I felt a bit better. I heard Mum and Dad go to bed so I crept downstairs again to phone Peter to tell him all about my evening. I had to force my brain to concentrate on what he was saying. "I love you, Sarah but you really shouldn't go out with 'worldlies'."

"Love you too, Peter. G'night." I ignored the second part of his remark and it wasn't till later that I remembered it.

When I'd dragged myself upstairs again, I couldn't be bothered to undress so I crept under the eiderdown and hoped I wouldn't feel too bad the next day. I knew I shouldn't have drunk so much – but it had been so hard to refuse!

The next day I didn't have to go to work fortunately. I had a splitting headache and I must have looked awful because Mum didn't say anything. I didn't feel like going out and Rachel was in our room so I went into Tim's room for some privacy. I knew he wouldn't be there. I didn't know where he was. He was as fed up as I was and he was just as rebellious but they didn't go on at him as much as they did at me. I wished I was a boy. Perhaps life would be easier.

As I flopped down on his bed, I kicked something. I looked down under the bed and picked up a small square machine. It was a cassette player! How had Tim managed to keep it hidden? I pressed the 'play' button and immediately I was transported to another world. The most beautiful sound in the world was filling the room. I clicked it off and took out the tape. It was one of the Beatles' songs. I'd heard of them because everyone at school had talked about them but I'd never heard their music. I was hooked. I replaced the tape and turned down the volume. Then I lay on the bed and let the sound wash over me. It was so uplifting to listen to such wonderful 'real' music. I'd never heard anything like it. It was like eating honey after salt.

Over the next few days whenever I could, I sneaked into Tim's bedroom and listened to his tapes. He had quite a collection. I didn't say anything to him in case anyone heard us talking.

As usual we didn't do anything special at Christmas and then it was back to work. One lunch hour I ventured into Dixon's and bought myself a small radio. I was still a bit scared as I knew the Brethren would disapprove but I didn't see anything wrong in it and I'd be able to listen to my beloved music whenever I wanted to. It made all the years of not having one worthwhile. I kept it well hidden but sometimes I walked around with it hidden under my jumper. I loved listening to all the different groups. How had I existed before I discovered music? It became the highlight of my life and helped me to cope with the increasing difficulties with the Brethren.

Crowds of new rules were suddenly introduced. Of course they all affected me! At one evening Meeting Tony Bates read out a list of items that were now to be banned from our houses and we were not to use. Televisions and computors were already on the list but when he announced the new banned items, I thought he must be joking. He wasn't!

"Mr Finch has announced that bicycles are no longer to be used. Brothers and sisters must use cars or walk to the Meetings."

I cycled everywhere. I wasn't going to give up my bike. I seethed. Fortunately that 'rule' was never implemented. Books were next on the list. Books?

"Mr Finch has also instructed that all books not written by Brethren are to be burnt."

I felt sick. I loved reading. It was an escape from the restrictions of my life and through reading I had discovered there was another 'world' out there. My mind buzzed. How could I hide my 'library'? I certainly wasn't going to burn my beloved books. That would be wicked. What right had the Brethren to govern every aspect of our lives? God had given us brains but we weren't allowed to use them. Was I the only one who felt rebellious? I wasn't! There were others of my age who felt the same.

Surreptitiously a black market in novels started after some brothers had insisted on having bonfires as instructed. Fortunately Dad liked books as much as I did and he allowed us to keep them as long as they remained out of sight of any Brethren visitors.

"I've got a copy of 'Wuthering Heights'," Katie hissed at me one Sunday in the car park after the six o'clock Meeting. "Do you want to exchange it for one of Georgette Heyer's?"

It seemed a fair exchange. "I'll bring it this afternoon," I muttered. Katie made sure no one was looking at us before handing me 'Wuthering Heights'. I couldn't wait to start it.

I didn't have a chance to read it until the following Tuesday evening when I was babysitting for the Grays.

They had two small children and wanted to go to the evening Meeting together so I said I'd babysit. The children were sweet and I played with them and put them to bed before settling down to read the 'forbidden' book which I'd hidden in my bag. It was gripping and I was horrified when I heard the key in the lock. Surely they weren't home already. What could I do? I'd be in more trouble if they knew what I'd been reading.

"Have the children behaved themselves, Sarah?" Mr Gray came into the room and I hurriedly hid the book behind my back. I'd left my bag in the hall.

"Yes, they were fine," I gabbled. "Excuse me. I have to go to the loo."

Rushing past him, I shot up the stairs to lock myself in the bathroom. Then I systematically shredded Emily Bronte's classic into the pan, frequently flushing it. It took ages and I hoped the Grays would think I'd got diarrhoea. When the last speck of paper had disappeared, I opened the door and went downstairs trying to look ill. Mrs Gray was sympathetic and I was soon on my way home. I was annoyed I hadn't even finished reading the book. I hoped Katie wouldn't be too mad. I'd have to buy her another copy!

In spite of my escape, I still borrowed and leant books 'on the black market'. The element of risk made it quite exciting but fortunately I didn't get caught.

But Dad discovered my radio one day. He was furious and confiscated it. I was so miserable because it had been a lifeline for me. But I knew he wasn't happy either and it was my fault – mine and Tim's. I overheard Tony Bates telling Dad it was all his fault his family was so rebellious.

"You're not controlling them properly," he said looking as if butter wouldn't melt in his mouth. "They need more discipline."

I could see Dad was mad but he didn't say anything. But he was angry with us when he came home.

"You're giving us all a bad name," he complained. "Why can't you do as you're told and not always break the rules."

"Because life's one long rule," I groaned. "We're not allowed to think for ourselves or have any fun."

The next day Rachel was crying when she came home from school.

"No one will speak to me," she sobbed. "They say I'm a bad influence. And it's all your fault. I try to be good."

"You are," I said trying to put my arm round her but she shook me off and ran, crying, up the stairs.

We were all shouting at each other. Our happy family seemed to be breaking up. Surely that couldn't be right, could it? I was beginning to feel like a piece of string being pulled in two directions at once. No one in the Meeting would have anything to do with me as I was such a bad influence. I often wore jeans and even my other clothes were more colourful and 'different' from other sisters. I even sometimes talked to 'worldlies'. If it hadn't been for Eileen, I think I'd have snapped in two.

"Christianity shouldn't make people so miserable, should it?" I asked her. "You're not miserable, are you? Your Church doesn't make rules and regulations which govern every bit of your life, does it?"

"No. We just try to follow Christ's example," she said gently.

"But that's what the Brethen say. But they're so hypocritical. Jesus didn't condemn anyone because they broke all the religious laws, did he?"

"I don't think he thought the rules were very important. He did criticise the Pharisees for making so much of the outward ritual. He said it was what went on in a person's heart that mattered."

"Yes," I said thoughtfully. "He was so gentle with everyone – even those who'd done wrong."

The following Sunday I was so depressed I refused to go to the Meeting.

"You have to go, Sarah," said Dad. "You can't be trusted to be left on your own."

"I'm nearly seventeen," I retorted. "I don't see why you both have to follow me everywhere. I'm sick of not having any freedom. And I don't see why I should waste my day going to a place where people hate me."

"Don't be silly, Sarah," said Mum. "Of course they don't hate you."

"Oh yes, they do." I was well into my stride now. "Whenever I walk into the Meeting, I feel a wave of hostility hit me. If I make an effort to be friendly, I always get a cold stare so what's the point?"

I rushed out of the house. I was in such a terrible rage I knew I had to get away before I said something I might regret. I ran down the road to the bus shelter and sat there crying my eyes out. I always went there when I was upset. It was my little haven of peace and I soon regretted I'd been rude to Mum and Dad. But it didn't alter the way I felt. I had to do something about my life. It was such a mess.

When I got back to the house, it was empty. Everyone else had gone to the Meeting. A plan was forming in my mind. I had to do something! I found Eileen's phone number. It was too early for her to have gone to Church. As I waited for her to answer, I kept looking over my shoulder to make sure no one came in. I knew it was silly as the rest of the family wouldn't be home for hours.

"Hullo."

"Eileen? It's Sarah. Do you think I could come with you to your Church this evening? I'd really like to."

"Of course you can," she said warmly. "Shall I pick you up?"

"Oh no," I said quickly. "You tell me where it is and I'll cycle there."

"I'll look out for you and save you a seat. It gets quite crowded."

She gave me directions and I put the phone down realising my hands were trembling. What had I done?

I wondered if I would go or would I chicken out? I sat on the stairs and shut my eyes.

"Please Lord Jesus," I whispered, "Could you tell me if it's all right to go to the New Wine Fellowship. I feel so guilty."

Gradually I felt the tension leave me and a feeling of peace enveloped me. It was a wonderful feeling.

"Oh thank you," I whispered. I was sure Jesus was saying it was all right to go.

I decided to be 'good' for the rest of the day and when Mum and Dad came back, I said I was sorry and went to the next two Meetings. But my mind felt like milk being churned. Should I go to the New Wine Fellowship? Or not? What excuse would I give this time for not going to the last Meeting of the day?

But when the evening came, Mum made it easy for me. "Are you feeling all right, Sarah?" she asked. "You look a bit pale."

"I've got a splitting headache," I lied. "Do you mind if I stay in this evening?"

I hated lying but I couldn't help it. To my surprise even Dad raised no objection. I waited until they'd left and then went quickly to get my bike before I could change my mind. The die was cast. I felt scared and guilty but also exhilarated.

What would it be like?

CHAPTER SEVEN

⌘

AT PEACE WITH GOD

Teach me to do your will, for you are my God;
may your good Spirit lead me on level ground.
[Psalm 143:10]

I found the church with no difficulty and parked
my bike. Eileen was waiting just inside the door and
introduced me to some people. They all shook hands
and said how glad they were to see me. It was so
different from the Meeting. When we went inside, it
was so noisy! I couldn't believe it. But everyone looked
happy. In the Meeting you could hear a pin drop and
no one ever smiled!

That evening was the most wonderful experience of
my life. To my amazement there were crowds of young
people there. They prayed and worshipped so devot-
edly. How different from the young people in the
Brethren. Sometimes I wondered if some of them knew
anything about God and what he had done for them. It

always made me cringe when any of them mocked Christianity. It was so sad that, although they were in the Brethren, I felt some of them weren't Christians.

The preacher at the New Wine Fellowship was quite young. He talked about the Lord Jesus and what he had done for us by dying on the Cross and defeating death by rising again. Then he referred to the return of the Lord Jesus and Judgement Day when we will have to account for our lives. I squirmed a bit because I had lied to Mum and Dad. I resolved to tell them the truth when I got home. In this atmosphere I could have done anything.

I felt at peace with God and had the trememdous joy of knowing he loved me. His presence surrounded me and I felt the most wonderful elation at being free to worship him. All around me people were singing and dancing and soon I was drawn into this worship of the Creator God and his Son, Jesus. At one point I broke down in tears as I realised God had given me such a clear sign there were many other Christians on earth besides the Brethren.

All the way home, I was wondering how to tell Mum and Dad. I knew they'd be horrified. They were!

"How can you even think of associating with such wicked people?" stormed Dad.

"But they're not wicked," I cried. "They truly love the Lord Jesus and worship him. It was such a marvellous feeling to be with them. I felt as though I was in Heaven."

"Sarah, that's blasphemy!" gasped Mum.

"It isn't! It's true. Oh I wish you'd been there. How can you be so blind?"

How could I get through to them? They seemed to think that because someone had sinned, he or she should be denied access to God. But that was why Jesus came to die – so that we could have access to his Father, God. Jesus didn't shut anyone out – not like the Brethren who considered themselves so 'holy' they couldn't associate with anyone else. But if people love the Lord Jesus, there's no barrier at all. Why couldn't Mum and Dad understand that?

"You're not to go again, Sarah. That's an order. How could you do this to us?" Dad stamped out of the room. He reappeared a few moments later, holding in his hand the canvas bag I'd just given him for his birthday. He threw it at me.

"I can't accept this from such a disobedient daughter," he snarled.

I was heartbroken. He needed a bag to store his tools and I'd spent ages choosing it. How could he be so cruel to me? I started to cry and rushed upstairs hurling the bag under my bed.

That night I couldn't sleep. All the upset and arguments had got to me. I lay awake till half past three wondering how on earth I could get Mum and Dad to see the truth. Then I worried because I wanted to shout God's name aloud and tell everyone what he'd done for me but I was too cowardly. I wished, too, I didn't lose my temper so quickly with Mum and Dad. I knew that wouldn't bring them to my way of thinking.

In spite of Mum and Dad I went to the New Wine Fellowship again a few weeks later on a lovely April evening. It was different this time but just as inspiring. A group of gypsies, who travelled the world preaching, told us about their experiences in Ireland and sang some lovely songs. They asked if anyone would be willing to do a door to door collection to support a charity which was helping the starving children of Ethiopia.

Afterwards I spoke to one of them and said I'd help. She smiled. "Thank you so much. We've got some tins here and here's a badge for you. What's your name?"

"Sarah Foster."

She wrote it down on her list and on the badge and I felt excited that I was at last going to do something to help people who were in such need. When I got home, I hid the collecting tin under my bed and after work the next day, I knocked at the doors of the houses in the streets I'd been given. Some of them slammed the door in my face but others listened when I told them about the collection and they put in some money.

Of course Dad was crossing the hall when I got home.

"What have you got there, Sarah?" he demanded.

I tried to hide the tin behind my back but it was no good. He grabbed hold of it.

"Orphans in Ethiopia? What's this?" He glared at me.

"I was collecting some money to help the starving children of Ethiopia," I muttered.

"How dare you take part in something that's organised by the world!"

"Well we don't help anyone in need, do we?" I exclaimed. "We all have our cosy little lives and don't care at all about the awful things that are happening around us. Why don't we send out missionaries to tell people about Jesus? Why don't we collect money to help the poor? Why.....?"

"That's enough, Sarah. You're not to do this any more and you're to return the tin."

"I've collected some money anyway," I shouted as I grabbed it and ran upstairs. "That's more than you've ever done."

A few minutes later I regretted what I'd said. It wasn't Dad's fault. He'd just been brainwashed into thinking everything the Brethren said and did was right. How I wished I could show him there were other Christians in the world.

I took the collecting tin to work the next day and gave it to Eileen explaining what had happened.

"I'm not surprised," she said. "I wondered if you'd be allowed to do it."

"Things are getting worse," I groaned. "Everything I do is wrong. I've got this friend, Peter, and I really like him. He was a rebel like me and we have a lot in common. But he's changed lately. He's getting more disapproving of things I do. I think he wants to marry me but I don't love him enough."

"Then you mustn't marry him."

"I know but it's easy to say that." Peter was becoming quite a problem. When I was younger, it was great to have a boy friend who kissed me and made a fuss of me. But now I didn't like him kissing me and I wasn't sure I loved him any more.

He'd come down to see me a week ago although I hadn't wanted him to and from my point of view the whole evening had been a disaster. He'd taken me to see a horror film and I'd hated it. It was so horrid I'd tried not to watch and prayed, "Dear God, please help me to take no notice of this."

When he took me home, he drove like a maniac and I wouldn't let him kiss me so he went off in a huff. Although he still went to cinemas and restaurants, he was also trying to be a 'respectable' young brother so I felt he was hypocritical. I must have grown out of him, I thought sadly. I certainly didn't want to marry him and be trapped for ever in the Meeting.

On Sunday Katie grabbed hold of me during the 'Break' and said she'd got something to tell me. She'd just come back from some three day Meetings in Sweden so I wasn't surprised when she said she'd 'met someone'.

"Is he nice?"

"He's lovely," she sighed. "But he's Swedish. I'd have to live over there. I'm applying for Swedish citizenship."

"Good gracious!" I wondered how the Swedish authorities would react to this whirlwind 'romance'. "I'll miss you."

Katie was a pain sometimes but she was the only real friend I had in the Brethren. If she left, I'd really be on my own.

"I'll miss you, too."

Later I heard about her interview with the Swedish authorities. As I'd expected, they weren't impressed.

"How long have you known him?"

"Two weeks."

"How many times have you met him?"

"Once."

"How long for?"

"Two hours."

"How many more times will you see him before your wedding?"

"None."

I wasn't surprised they turned down her application. The Brethren decided she'd better meet him again before she re-applied. I'd have given up. She couldn't know him properly. At least I knew Peter enough to know I couldn't marry him. Unfortunately, now he'd started to change into a 'respectable brother', Mum and Dad thought he'd be a good match for me. He would 'be a good influence'. They obviously didn't know he still went to the cinema and watched horror films!

"But I thought you liked Peter," said Mum plaintively one evening as we were doing the washing up. "You always made such a fuss when we wouldn't let you meet him."

"I've changed, Mum – and so's he. I wouldn't be happy. I know I wouldn't. You don't want me to be unhappy, do you?"

"Of course I don't."

I didn't add that I didn't want to be trapped either. I felt in such a muddle about everything. I couldn't imagine myself still with the Brethren in fifty years' time. But at the moment I couldn't see any way out. And I didn't want to end up like Denise Long. She'd recently married but was living with her in-laws as her husband spent every free moment building their house. She hardly ever saw him and as she'd moved away from her own area, she'd lost all her friends and I'd heard she was very lonely and unhappy. That sort of life wasn't for me.

The following evening when I came home, I found a letter waiting for me. It was really weird. It read:

```
Dear Sarah,
        I've been thinking about you a lot
these last few days. I presume you
know how I feel about you. Please
write back to tell me if you're inter-
ested in me or not. I think it would
be great if we were to get to know
each other better. I assume you know
why this is happening.
                Love,
                Clive.
```

It didn't make sense. I didn't know anyone called Clive. I re-read it and then looked at the address. I became more and more puzzled. Then I had a thought and cold shivers ran all over me. The only Clive I knew who came from that area was a married brother with three children. Surely it couldn't be him. My hands were shaking as I grabbed the address book on the hall table and looked up the surname. It couldn't be the same! It was! I collapsed on the stairs feeling sick. What was I to do?

"Whatever's the matter, Sarah?" I hadn't heard Mum come in.

I burst into tears and handed her the letter. "It's from Clive Saunders," I sobbed. "I've just checked the address."

"Oh dear, oh dear." Mum was as shocked as I was. "We'll have to tell Dad. He'll know what to do."

Dad was horrified. "There's no reason for Clive to think like this, is there, Sarah? You've never encouraged him, have you?"

"Of course I haven't," I sobbed. "I'd never look at a married man." I put my hands over my face as Mum put her arm round me and Dad picked up the phone to call Tony Bates.

Of course he came round straight away and I was grilled on my appearance, my relationships and anything else he could think of. It was my fault, apparently, and nothing to do with Clive. I couldn't believe it.

"What a pity you wear such suggestive clothing, Sarah," he said sombrely. "It leads brothers astray."

"I don't know what you mean. I just wear ordinary clothes."

"But your blouses have low necks. You know they should have high collars. And your skirts are too short."

I was seething. "So it's all my fault, is it? I haven't done anything, I tell you. I couldn't even work out for ages who the letter was from."

He looked a bit taken aback. "All right, Sarah, don't get upset. We'll look into it."

But they didn't, of course. I couldn't face going to the Meeting that weekend. I knew they'd all be looking at me and talking about me. I'd prayed for a sign to show whether it was right for me to leave the Brethren. Perhaps the letter and the Brethen's reaction to it was the sign I'd been waiting for.

When I went to work on Monday, Eileen said quietly, "What's the matter, Sarah?"

"Nothing," I said quickly. I always tried to put a good face on at work but obviously it hadn't worked this time.

"Yes there is," she insisted. "I always know when you're not happy. Do you want to tell me what's happened?"

I did – and I didn't. In the end I told her about the letter.

"I'm just so fed up," I groaned. "My whole life's being wrecked by this – 'religion'. And that shouldn't happen, should it?"

"Of course not." She paused for a moment and gave me a thoughtful look. "Sarah, I want you to promise me something. If you really find you can't take any more, you're very welcome to come and stay with me."

I was stunned. How kind she was. "Oh, Eileen, that's the nicest thing anyone's ever said to me."

"Well bear it in mind if you're desperate."

"I will," I promised. Suddenly things didn't look quite so bad after all. I had a lifeline.

When I got home, I was furious to find my secret diary had been taken out from its hiding place. That meant someone had read it! I'd put down all my angry feelings about the way I was treated so I hoped the reader felt guilty. No one said anything so I never found out who it was.

The next day we heard on the grapevine my brother Richard and his wife had had a baby girl. Mum cried all day because he hadn't phoned to tell us himself. When Dad phoned to ask him why, he said it was "because Sarah refuses to go to the Meetings". Everything was always my fault. I felt really miserable.

Janice Hawes phoned me at work and asked me to go round to see her. She said she had something important to tell me. I assumed it would be about my cousins but it wasn't. When I got there, she was in a real state.

"Oh, Sarah, I'm so glad you've come. I was afraid you wouldn't."

"Why?"

"I met your mother and she told me I wasn't to have anything to do with you."

"She had no right to do that," I said angrily.

"I feel awful disobeying her but I had to see you. Bill thinks I'm taking it too seriously."

"What?" I was getting alarmed.

"I had this awful dream about you and I felt I had to tell you as I think it's a warning. I dreamt you were in prison, terribly distressed and they were trying to marry you off to someone. Then I woke up but it seemed so real. I've been biting my nails to the quick with worry. I was so relieved when I heard you at work. I thought something might have happened to you."

"I suppose it's true in a way," I said thoughtfully. "I'm certainly in a prison and very unhappy."

"Poor Sarah."

Yes. 'Poor Sarah', I thought as I cycled home. What a mess my life was. Would it ever get sorted out? At dinner that night Dad said he'd had a phone call from Clive Saunders. I felt sick and pushed my dinner away.

"He asked my forgiveness for what he'd done and told me to tell you he was sorry, Sarah. Will you accept that?"

"No," I snapped. "I never want to see him again. I can't stand the sight of him and I refuse to go to any Meetings if he's going to be there."

"That's not very nice, Sarah," reproved Mum.

"What he did wasn't very 'nice' and I got all the blame for it. Nothing's ever been done to him, has it? He's still in favour." There was no answer to that because it was true. I was the one who was in trouble.

The following Sunday there was another almighty row because I refused again to go the Meeting because I knew Clive Saunders would be there. Mum and Dad kept on and on at me. They kept telling me how selfish I was. In the end they gave up and left me and I thought about my future. I was sure my time with the Brethren was drawing to a close and I prayed that God would show me the right path to follow. I almost felt angrier at being blamed for what had happened than I did about Clive's actual letter.

While everyone was out, I decided to look for the radio Dad had confiscated. I knew it was wrong of me to go through his desk but he shouldn't have taken my radio.

While I was hunting for it, I found something that really disturbed me. Inside one of the drawers was a bunch of letters. The writing looked familiar and I drew them out. They were from my Grandad Foster. I knew I shouldn't but I had to read them and later I wished I hadn't. They made me so sad and I was crying when I finished. Grandad had written them because his wife was ill and he was pleading for Dad to go and visit her before she died. Of course Dad never did see her and the last letter informed him of her death. It ended, "Her every hope was that her next visitor would be her dear son but it was not to be."

I couldn't read the rest for the tears were streaming down my face. How could people, who called themselves Christians, be so unloving? That was what would happen to me, I thought unhappily. If I left, they would shut me off completely. I didn't blame Dad for what had happened. I was sure he hadn't really wanted to cut off his parents. He'd been pressured into it.

I was becoming more and more convinced I had to leave even if it meant losing my family. God was giving me clear signs that the whole system of the Brethren had gone drastically wrong. My most heartfelt prayer was that God would show me the right path and that my family might join me on it so that my vow would be fulfilled.

Putting the letters back, I stared into space not able to concentrate on anything. My poor grandparents. How I wished I'd known my grandmother. How sad she must have been not to have seen Dad before she died.

When the others came back, I was almost back to normal. I didn't mention the letters to anyone except Tim who'd gone to the Meeting like a good boy. When he came in, he went straight up to his room and I followed him.

Tears formed in his eyes as I told him what I'd discovered.

"How can they behave like this? It's not Christian, is it?"

"No it's not. What was it like this morning?"

"Awful as usual. Oh, Clive Saunders preached."

"What? I don't believe it."

"I thought you'd find that interesting and there are all sorts of rumours flying around about you because you don't go to the Meeting. They think you've done something awful and of course it's all your fault and you'd got it coming to you – or something like that."

"Thanks, Tim."

"Oh I'm sorry, Sarah. I didn't mean it to come out like that. I'm just so angry about it all. I tried to stick up for you but it's like bashing your head against a brick wall. I gave up in the end."

"Thanks for trying anyway. I'm glad you told me. Actually I'm quite pleased. I feel that's one more sign God has given me to show how wrong they are. I can't believe that Clive Saunders was given the 'special privilege' of preaching after what he did. It just shows there's one rule for him and another for me. I'll always be the scapegoat."

139

"It certainly looks like that," Tim agreed.

As Spring turned into Summer, I meditated on my future. I wanted to leave the Brethren but I needed someone to give me a nudge. Then one hot June day, my cousin, Tessa, phoned me at work. Fortunately we weren't very busy and we talked for ages. It was the first time I'd spoken to her – apart from the funeral. She sounded really sweet and I was so thrilled to hear from her.

"I'm staying with Mum and Dad for a few days," she told me. "They've just moved into Grandad's house. There's still a lot of work to do on it but it's going to be really nice. I wondered if we might meet some time. I could pick you up from work."

"That would be great."

I hoped I'd recognise her. I'd only met her once and she'd been wearing a hat!

"How about tomorrow? We could go out for a meal somewhere."

"I'd like that."

That evening I told Mum I was working late the next day. I hated lying to her but I knew she'd have a fit if she knew what I was doing.

I was really nervous as I waited for Tessa. Suppose someone saw us. But my cousin had thought of that. As she screeched to a halt beside me and I opened the door, she hissed, "Get in the back and throw the car rug over you and then no one'll see you."

I giggled as I obeyed her and I felt as if I was being kidnapped. I'd no idea where we were going. At last we stopped and I crawled out. The wind hit my face and it had started to rain. We seemed to be in the country. Hills rolled away on to the horizon.

"Come on. We'll have something to eat."

I realised we were in the car park of a 'Little Chef'. I'd never been to one before and realised I was hungry. But I was more hungry to talk to my cousin and ask her advice about my future. She was a good listener.

"I don't think I can take much more of it," I sighed. "I really think the time has come for me to leave."

"I think you should," she said thoughtfully. "Take up Eileen's offer and stay with her for a few days. You could look on it as a holiday."

"I hate the thought of leaving Mum and Dad. I'd rather die than hurt them but I'm sure God is telling me this is the right time to go. I knew it would happen some time."

"I don't suppose your parents are really happy about things either," she said shrewdly.

"No," I said thoughtfully. I told her about the vow I'd made at our grandad's grave and her eyes filled with tears.

"I'm sure God will help you to fulfil it," she said.

"I do hope so. It is my dearest wish."

She drove me back, still huddled under the car rug and dropped me round the corner from my home.

"Don't forget. You're to tell Eileen tomorrow."

"I will." I waved and ran off. I was relieved no one questioned me on that occasion.

Eileen was delighted when I told her I'd like to stay with her for a few days.

"That's marvellous," she said. "I'm sure it's the right thing. When do you want to come?"

"How about a week on Wednesday? That will give me time to decide what I'm bringing with me and how I'm going to explain to Mum and Dad."

"What will you tell them?"

"The truth I think but I don't want them to know until the last possible moment. And I shan't tell them where I'm going in case they drag me back."

"I'm sure they wouldn't do that."

"They might."

That evening Peter phoned and I told him my plans. "I really can't cope with this pressure any more, Peter," I explained. "Everything goes wrong and everyone hates me. I can't wait to get away."

"Oh stop being so negative, Sarah," he said crossly. "Why don't you look for the good things in the Brethren?"

"What good things?"

"Well....."

"I thought you understood, Peter. Anyway, I'm going and that's that." I slammed down the phone.

I thought I could trust him even though he'd changed recently. But he betrayed me. I couldn't believe it. He told his Mum and of course she told mine. I was so furious with him. How dared he fool me into thinking he was my friend.

The next few days were terrible. I felt as though I was in Hell. Mum kept crying and Dad wouldn't speak to me. When Wednesday came, I was still determined to leave. I'd hidden my case under the bed and hoped I'd be able to get out of the house before anyone saw me. Of course everything went wrong again.

As I crept downstairs in the evening with the telltale case in my hand, Dad come out of the front room. I started to shake and I could feel the hairs prick at the back of my neck.

"Come in here, Sarah," he said sternly.

I tried to say something but I couldn't and I meekly followed him into the room. Then I nearly died. Facing me were Tony Bates, Brian Forbes, and Mum and Dad. They all stared solemnly at me as I collapsed on the nearest chair. So I was to have a real 'priestly' as we called them. I was surprised I'd never had one before and I dreaded it. It felt like being in a torture chamber waiting for the pain to begin.

There was a long pause while everyone just stared at me. I knew that was part of their plan to break me down but I took a deep breath and thought of the Lord Jesus. He'd had to face 'high priests' but I was sure he'd never subject anyone to the inquisition I was about to undergo.

At last Tony Bates cleared his throat. "So you want to leave us, Sarah," he intoned.

"Yes." My voice came out like a squeak.

"The Devil stalks the world seeking whom he may devour. Aren't you afraid of that, Sarah?"

My mouth was dry. Yes, of course I was afraid. Sometimes the 'world', seemed like a lion's open mouth into which I was about to walk. But the 'cage' that enclosed me was even worse. I had to break free.

"Sarah?"

I took a deep breath. "There are lots of other Christians in the 'world' as you call it. They love the Lord Jesus and they worship him freely. Why do you think you're the only ones who are right?"

"We are told to 'come out from among them and be separate'."

"But Jesus said, 'Be in the world but not of it.' That's different, isn't it?"

I was gaining confidence. I was so sure God was showing me it was right to leave – at least for a time. But I was only seventeen and the pressure on me was so tremendous, it felt like a block of concrete weighing me down.

For five hours they pounded me, telling me I was wicked, selfish and ungrateful and that if I left, I'd never see my family again and I'd be cut off from all 'fellowship'. I couldn't stand it and by the end I hardly knew what I was saying. I was so tired I felt really ill.

They left at last and to my astonishment, I realised I'd convinced them I was going.

But my ordeal wasn't over. It was my parents' turn. "Please, Sarah, don't leave us," pleaded Mum. "What will we do without you? We'll never see you again. I can't bear it."

"You know this is the end, Sarah, don't you?" Dad stressed. "If you leave now, you'll never come back."

Tears were pouring down my face. I thought I was going mad. I'd been so sure I was doing the right thing but how could I leave Mum and Dad and my brother and sister and never see them again? In the end I'd had enough.

"All right," I said wearily. "I'll stay for one more week and see if things change."

I hardly slept at all that night and was surprised I managed to get to work the next day.

Eileen was very upset I'd changed my mind. She'd been looking forward to my visit.

"I'm so sorry, Eileen. I just couldn't take any more. But I've said I'll only stay for another week to see if things improve."

They didn't, of course. Nothing changed but I prayed that if it was now right to stay, God would give me a sign. But nothing happened. Then Bill Hawes phoned and said he wanted to talk to me. When I went round to see him after work, he told me he and Janice were very concerned about me.

"We know you're having a hard time, Sarah and we want to help you. We've got a house in Cornwall and we wondered if you'd like to go there for a week to get away from everything."

"Oh, Bill, that would be wonderful!" I exclaimed. "I tried to leave last week but Mum and Dad found out and persuaded me not to go. I said I'd stay for a week to see if anything changed. It hasn't, so I'm sure this is an answer to prayer."

"We'll drive you down on Friday and keep you company over the weekend and then you can stay on as long as you like."

"Thank you so much. It's really kind of you."

This time I was determined nothing was going to go wrong. I certainly wasn't going to tell Peter. I didn't trust him any more.

Every night I added a little more to my suitcase whenever Rachel wasn't in the room. Outside the window of our bedroom was a flat roof and below that was an alley way between our house and that of our neighbours. On Wednesday night when everyone was asleep, I carefully attached some strong rope to the handle of the case and lowered it out of the window on to the roof. Then, glancing nervously at Rachel to make sure she wasn't stirring, I clambered after it. It was a warm June night and the moon was shining so I could see what I was doing. Dragging the suitcase to the edge of the roof, I grabbed hold of the rope and carefully lowered it to the ground. It would be hidden till the morning when I would pick it up. I hoped it wouldn't rain. Having successfully accomplished my mission, I climbed back, quietly closed the window and crept into bed. Rachel hadn't stirred.

I'd recently passed my driving test and had bought a car so I was able to slip the case into the boot without anyone noticing. I took it to work where I would leave it overnight ready for the Friday.

It was a good thing I did as Dad decided to take my car to pieces to fix a funny noise it was making so I was without a car on Friday and would have had real problems lugging a suitcase to work!

I didn't sleep much Thursday evening and the next morning I felt very unsettled. I made sure I said 'goodbye' to everyone before I went to work although they didn't know it was to be a longer 'goodbye' than they anticipated. I felt very emotional but tried to behave normally. I wondered how long it would be before I saw them again – or even if I would.

At lunch time I went into the Library to write a letter to Mum and Dad. As I sat at the table, tears poured down my cheeks and I could hardly see to write. It was one of the most upsetting times of my life. I knew I was going to hurt my parents badly and I didn't want to because I loved them so much. But I had to get away. I tried to explain why I had to leave them and asked them to forgive me, telling them I'd never forget them whatever happened. It took me ages to write and I so hoped they'd understand but I doubted it. I was going to send the note via Interflora with a lovely bunch of flowers for Mum.

Clutching the letter, I hurried out of the Library and bumped straight into her!

"Sarah!" she exclaimed. "What are you doing here? I thought you always had your lunch at work. Are you all right?"

"Yes. Yes. Of course I am," I babbled. "I just – had to look something up – for work. I must dash now. I'm late! 'Bye."

"Bye, dear. See you tonight."

It was a good thing she couldn't see my face as it was looking like Niagara Falls. Sobbing, I ran into the florist and ordered the most expensive bunch of flowers I could afford.

"And please put this letter with them," I gasped. "Can you make sure they're delivered about five this afternoon?"

"Certainly, Madam."

I ran back to the office where Bill and Janice were waiting for me. I'd got the afternoon off as well as the following week and when Mum received the flowers and the letter, I'd be miles away on my way to Cornwall.

As we drove towards the west, I was completely distraught. I no longer knew whether I was doing the right thing and the thought that I might never see my family again made me feel physically sick.

Bill eventually drew into a layby as I was cryng so much I'd almost caused him to have an accident.

"Would you like to go back, Sarah?" asked Janice turning round to look at me. She looked so concerned.

"No – yes – I don't know," I wailed.

She got out of the car and opened the back door. Sitting beside me, she put her arms round me as I continued to sob. Eventually I calmed down a little and she said quietly, "I think it would do you good to get away for a few days, Sarah. Then when you're ready, we'll bring you back."

I nodded and Bill eased the car back into the traffic.

CHAPTER EIGHT

⌘

BRIEF ESCAPE

The eternal God is your refuge, and underneath are the everlasting arms.
[Deuteronomy 33:27]

That weekend was one of the most exciting of my life but I was still very unhappy about Mum and Dad. The house was lovely and I had a bedroom overlooking the sea and a cliff path led down to the beach. I phoned home soon after we arrived. Dad picked up the phone immediately so I knew he must have been waiting by it. I started to cry again.

"Where are you, Sarah?" He sounded upset.

"I'm all right," I insisted.

"You're to come home right now." He was annoyed now he knew I was all right. "How dare you go away without telling us where you were going. You're under age. You have no right to leave us. You're to come home – now."

"I can't do that, Dad. I need some space and freedom to think. I'm being well looked after. I'll call you tomorrow."

I put the phone down because I couldn't talk any more. I was crying and shaking. Bill led me into the kitchen where Janice had just made a cup of tea.

"I think it would be better not to phone again, Sarah," he said. "They know you're safe and well and it will only upset you. They'll continue to persuade you to return, won't they?"

I nodded, my lips trembling. "I can't go home – not yet at any rate."

Janice pushed a cup of tea over to me. "Drink this, dear and try and forget about everything while you're here. Just relax and have a good time."

I took her advice. On Saturday I went swimming with the children and then Bill took us out in the boat with his brother, Mark. In the afternoon I walked around the village; everyone was so friendly and kind. I met Bill's Mum, Julie, who was a lovely Christian lady, and she took me under her wing. I didn't phone home again.

That evening after supper Bill and I talked for ages. He seemed to be searching for a faith and he made me question my own beliefs. Because of his searching questions, I had to concentrate on what I believed from what I'd read in the Bible and not just what the Brethren had told me.

"How can you be so sure there's a God, Sarah?" he asked as we sat drinking our coffee.

"You've only got to look around you at the beautiful land God created. It couldn't have got here by accident; and who is it who makes nature come to life again in the Spring?"

"Mm. I suppose there must be a God but what about Heaven and all that?"

"Heaven's where God is and when we die, if we believe that Jesus died for us, we'll be with him there for always."

"And if you don't believe?"

"Then you'll be without him for eternity. The Bible calls it Hell."

He looked uncomfortable. "Maybe it's a good idea to believe when you're getting old – just in case."

"You mean sort of take out an insurance as a safeguard."

"Yes."

"But you don't know when you're going to die, do you? You might be knocked down by a car tomorrow. It would be too late then."

We talked till about two in the morning and I found it very stimulating. I was sure he was playing Devil's Advocate some of the time because I thought he believed more than he admitted.

On Sunday I was invited by one of Mark's friends, Tom, to go out on his boat with a group of his friends.

I was thrilled and agreed to go but then Bill started to get all parental and put his foot down.

"I'd rather you didn't go, Sarah. I feel responsible for you. You've led such a sheltered life; you need to know the facts of life before you go out with a bunch of lads by yourself."

I was disappointed but I didn't want to argue; he'd been so good to me. Instead he took us all out in his boat. I tried to act as normally as possible but inside I was crying all the time about possibly losing my family. I knew before long, I'd have to think seriously about my future. I couldn't stay in Cornwall for ever.

Bill and Janice had to go back home in the afternoon but they said I could stay as long as I needed to. I didn't mind being in their lovely house all by myself and already I'd made lots of friends. I was invited out to dinner by one of them and when I went to bed that night, I thought how kind everyone had been. But they weren't my family and I missed my home so much.

It wasn't long before problems appeared. Julie, Bill's Mum, had invited me for lunch the next day and when I arrived, she told me she'd arranged for someone to meet me.

"I hope you don't mind, dear. I'm only trying to help. Evelyn goes to Christ Church and I thought she could have a little chat with you and help you to decide what to do."

My heart started pounding. I didn't want help. I had to sort out my own problems. As soon as people heard I'd left a religious sect, they immediately tried to get me to join another one! I didn't want to join anything yet. I wanted to be free.

"I don't want to talk to anyone yet, Julie," I said as gently as I could.

She looked disappointed. "I'm afraid she's already here."

It seemed I had no option. Evelyn had straight dark hair, wore no make up and was 'sensibly' dressed. She spoke in a very 'posh' accent and I didn't like her. For two hours she talked at me and by the end I was determined I'd never join the Church of England. With its robed clergy and altars, it was so far removed from everything I'd ever known.

She left at last and I spent the rest of the day with Julie trying to regain the feeling of tranquility I'd lost. But it didn't return and I felt as though an ominous black cloud was looming over me. I was right. The nightmare was about to start.

I walked home at ten o'clock. I was very tired and I'd just put on my nightdress and was brushing my hair when there was a banging at the door. My heart did a somersault into my mouth and for a moment I couldn't move. Then I heard Julie's voice.

"Sarah, Sarah, open the door – quickly."

I rushed down and flung it open and Julie almost fell inside, slamming it behind her. She was as white as the proverbial sheet and gasping for breath.

"Oh, Sarah, I'm so sorry. I had to come round straight away. I do hope they didn't follow me."

"Who?" I grabbed her arm. "What are you talking about, Julie?"

"Some – some people were asking for you. I – I said I'd never heard of you but I don't think they believed me. Oh dear. I hate lying but they kept on and on at me. Had I seen you? Was I sure I didn't know you?" She was badly shaken.

As soon as she'd spoken, I knew the Brethren were hot on my trail. How had they traced me? Had Peter put two and two together and come up with the right answer? He probably had. He'd betrayed me once. Was this really England in 1989? Why was I being hunted like a criminal?

"You'd better come back to my house, Sarah," Julie said. "I don't think they'll come back there. But I don't think you're safe here."

I nodded. "I'll come as soon as I'm ready. You go out the back way and I'll follow you in a minute."

I never had the chance. Before I'd even removed my nightdress, I heard a car. Peering through the curtains, I saw it sitting in the road outside the house in which I was now trapped. For a moment I panicked and then I remembered that from the back door a path led down to the beach. Hurriedly slipping my feet into the shoes I'd kicked off earlier, I let myself quietly out of the back door and ran down to the beach almost colliding with a dark figure which loomed up in front of me. I screamed and then wished I hadn't. I didn't want my pursuers to hear.

"Sarah, what on earth's the matter? What are you doing here at this time of night?" It was Mark.

"The Brethren are after me," I sobbed clinging to him. "They're outside the house. I came out the back way. I didn't even have time to change."

My teeth started chattering and I realised it was raining and I was already soaked. Mark didn't waste time.

"Quick. Hide under the boat. They won't see you there. I'll go and sort them out." He sounded very angry.

"Oh no don't – please – ."

But he'd gone so I crawled under the keel of the boat and shivered. It was pitch dark so I doubted if they would have been able to see me although I was wearing a white nightdress. I must look like a bedraggled ghost, I thought hysterically. Perhaps I should leap up and scare them away!

I heard footsteps on the gravel path and clenched my teeth to stop them chattering.

"Where is Sarah Foster?" It was Tony Bates' voice. "We know she's here and we have a right to talk to her."

"She has rights too, you know. She isn't here and even if she was, she wouldn't want to talk to you. Why don't you go away and leave her alone?"

"We want to see her."

"She's not here, I tell you. Now go away before I call the police and have you arrested for trespassing."

I'd no idea Mark could be so strong. He was determined to defend me and I was very grateful. I didn't think it was a private beach but Tony Bates wouldn't know that. I wondered which of his minions he'd brought with him. Then I heard another voice I recognised and I went cold all over. It was William Short – the chief 'priest' in England. Was I really so important they had to call on him? I was terrified and shaking with both cold and the fear that the 'priests' always inspired. They must be right, mustn't they? I'd been tricked by the Devil! I must go back! But I was too frightened to move. At last I heard their footststeps recede and then Mark peered under the boat.

"They've gone, Sarah. You can come out now. We'd better get you to Mum's before you catch pneumonia." Holding out his hand, he pulled me out and then putting his arm round me, he helped me up the path. We must have looked a strange couple.

Julie was waiting for me and she decided to ring Bill and ask him what to do. She'd obviously forgotten it was the middle of the night! But Bill didn't seem to mind although it took him ages to work out what was happening as Mark was on one phone and Julie on the other and they were both talking at once.

In the middle of all this chaos Julie's husband, Ray, came down. "What on earth's going on?" he demanded. "Don't you know it's the middle of the night?"

We were too busy to tell him what was happening so he just sat there, looking bemused. Then in the middle of her conversation with Bill, Julie suddenly looked at me and screamed.

"Good gracious, child, you're wet through. You'll catch your death. Come upstairs at once and we'll dry you out."

I was beginning to wonder if I was going mad. There was so much confusion everywhere and everyone was arguing about what I should do and where I should go while I was helpless in the middle of it all. I felt better after I'd had a hot bath and shrouded myself in one of Julie's dressing gowns.

When I went downstairs, everyone was discussing where I was to stay the rest of the night. There wasn't much left of it!

"This is Nigel. He lives at the other end of the village." Julie introduced a newcomer. I wondered where he'd sprung from. "He says he'll take you in his van to his house and you can spend the night there."

"That's very kind of you." I accepted a steaming mug of hot chocolate. Until a few days ago these people had all been strangers and now they were deeply concerned about my welfare. They were even losing a night's sleep because of me.

Julie leant me some clothes and gave me a dry nightdress and when I was respectable, she checked that no unwelcome visitors still lurked outside. Then Nigel and I sneaked out of the back door and I was bundled into his van. I felt as though I was the heroine in a spy thriller!

It was a short journey and when we reached his house, his wife, Ann, opened the door and a delicious smell wafted out.

"You must be hungry," she said. "I've made you some beans on toast."

Nothing had ever tasted so good. I hadn't realised how hungry I was. Emotion certainly took its toll and I did full justice to my early breakfast – or was it a late supper? The clock on the wall told me it was five to three but I'd got past feeling tired. However, when I was finally shown to my bed, I slept as soon as my head touched the pillow.

When I woke up, the sun was trying to burst through the curtains and I couldn't remember where I was. When I did, I hoped there'd be no more dramas. There was a cold cup of tea beside my bed and I wondered what the time was.

Hurriedly dressing, I went downstairs and found Ann in the kitchen.

"I'm sorry," I said shyly. "I'm afraid I overslept. Goodness. I'd no idea it was so late." It was nearly midday! I was very disorientated.

"We had to get up because of the children going to school."

"You must be tired. It was so kind of you to take me in last night."

"We were glad to help. We're so sorry to hear of your troubles."

"Thank you. I'm sure I'll be able to go back to Bill's house today. I shouldn't think the Brethren'll come back."

"I've talked to Julie this morning. She says Bill will phone you there later. Coffee?"

"Please." She filled me up with toast and coffee and then I walked back to Bill's house glancing nervously round to make sure no one was following me.

When I opened the front door, the phone was ringing and I rushed to answer it.

"Sarah? It's Bill. I've been ringing you all morning. Are you all right?"

"I'm fine. I overslept."

"Thank goodness. I was afraid you'd been kidnapped."

"What?"

"I talked to someone who left the Brethren last year and she said kidnapping wasn't out of the question."

"I don't think they'd go to those lengths," I said, horrified.

"Well be careful."

"Yes, I will."

"I've talked to your Mum and Dad but I can't make them understand. They blame me because you've left. I think they hate me." He sounded sad.

"That's silly, Bill. They should be grateful you're looking after me. I might have been murdered if I'd gone off on my own with nowhere to go."

"That's a bit melodramatic. I was glad to help. Sarah, we've decided you're not to go out alone. You must always have someone with you."

"Like a bodyguard?" I giggled.

"I'm serious. The Brethren have been down once. They may come again."

"Yes, I know, Bill. Thanks for all you've done and I promise I won't go out alone."

"Good girl. It would be better for you to stay with my Mum for the time being too. Do you mind?"

"Of course not – as long as she agrees."

I replaced the phone thoughtfully. I didn't really think the Brethren would kidnap me but they'd certainly use all their ammunition to pressure me to return and that would be a form of kidnap. Sadly, I realised the battle would go on until they forced me back. I'd always be plagued by them and they'd say things that would leave me no alternative but to return.

My feelings were confused. I felt guilty about leaving my family and I longed for their love and support but I didn't want to return to the 'prison' I'd left. I was sure God was still with me and helping me but he had blurred the future and I had no idea what would happen next. Would they come back for me?

I packed up my things and phoned Julie who picked me up in the car and took me shopping. For a while I was able to forget my problems.

In the afternoon I went out in a speedboat with Mark and one of his friends. I loved it. It was cold and the water was choppy but the sensation of flying through the frothy waves was exhilarating. I felt free at last. It was a marvellous feeling. Of course it didn't last.

Mark walked with me back to Julie's house and as we walked in, laughing and happy, there were Mum and Dad standing in the front room staring at me! There was no word of greeting or a smile – nothing. All my joy evaporated.

Julie had made a cup of tea and there was cake on a plate but of course they weren't eating with 'a worldly'. She looked embarrassed and stood up as we went in.

"We'll leave you alone. Come along, Mark."

After they'd gone, my heart felt as though it would burst right out of my chest. There stood the two people I loved most in the world but we were separated by a huge barrier erected by the Brethren. I knew Mum and Dad were hurting just as much as I was and I wanted so much to take away their pain. They were losing a daughter and I was losing my family. But although I wanted so desperately to return to them, I knew how wrong the Brethren were to cause this alienation. I realised that, with God's help, I had to be strong enough to break the chains that bound us all.

At last I couldn't stand the silence any longer and decided to take the initiative.

"Do sit down," I said, hastily. "I want to tell you that I love you more than anything but I can't go back with you. This is a different life. I'm free for the first time in my life and I need space and time to think and sort out my feelings."

"Please come home, Sarah." Mum was weeping. "Rachel's been crying ever since you left and Grandad's been ill and keeps asking for you."

"You know your place is with us, Sarah." Dad was angry but I was determined not to be swayed.

"If you loved me, you'd leave me here where I'm happy."

"You can't be happy with all these 'worldly' people. You have to come home."

"Your family needs you. I need you. Oh Sarah, please, please come home with us," pleaded Mum.

I'd had enough. "Stop it!" I shouted. "It's emotional blackmail and I won't give in to it. I'm staying here."

"No you're not." Dad was firm. "You're coming with us right now."

The pressure was mounting; I got up and moved over to the window and stared out. I was in the middle of a battle. On one side was my family whom I loved and on the other were all the people I'd come to love in the past few days. I looked out at God's beautiful land, at the white frothed waves on which a red boat was bobbing and the green cliffs below me.

Suddenly the sun came out and something inside me screamed, "I can't leave this beautiful place yet." Then another voice in my head shouted louder. "It's the Devil who wants you to stay." I started to panic. Everyone was trying to brainwash me into doing what they wanted, so I deliberately shut off my brain so I couldn't listen to Mum and Dad although part of me still wanted to go back with them. I felt torn apart.

"Nothing will make me come back with you," I told them at last, turning back from the window. Dad was very angry now and he came across to me and seized my arm. "We're leaving immediately. Come along, Sarah."

I was struggling to get away from him when the door flew open and in walked two police officers – a man and a woman! Was this all part of my nightmare? How had the police become involved? Dad dropped my arm and we all froze into a tableau. I wanted to die of shame. I discovered later that Bill had called the police when Julie told him my parents had turned up. He was afraid they might force me home against my will – which was just what they were doing.

"Perhaps you'd like to tell us what's going on." The woman police constable was very polite but they were obviously going to stay until they got some answers. She was looking at me.

I sat down near her. "I – I – don't want to go home," I whispered. "And Mum and Dad are trying to make me."

The policeman turned to Dad. "Is that correct, Sir?"

"She's our daughter and she's under age. She should be at home with us."

"How old are you, dear?" asked the woman police officer.

"Seventeen."

"Then you have no right to force her home against her will, Sir. The age at which she can legally leave home is sixteen. The only way you could keep her with you is to have her made a Ward of Court."

Mum was looking as if she couldn't believe this was happening. I started to cry. I could feel her pain as well as my own. The woman police officer handed me a tissue as her colleague told Dad they'd have to leave.

"Mrs Hawes has said she wants you off her property, Sir. If you refuse to go, I'm afraid I shall have to arrest you for trespass."

"There's no need for that." I could tell Dad was holding back his anger with difficulty. "We will leave and we won't force our daughter to go with us," he promised the police coldly.

"Very well, Sir, but I have to warn you we shall be keeping an eye on her as we believe she is being indoctrinated by a religious sect; we are concerned about her."

The Brethren would hate to be called 'a religious sect', I thought. Then I stared to shake. The woman police officer put her arm round me.

"Don't worry, dear. I'm sure everything will be all right."

I nodded but I knew it wouldn't. The pressure was becoming unbearable. Surely this wasn't what Christianity was all about. I was sure no true follower of Jesus Christ would subject a seventeen year old girl to this ordeal. Part of me even wanted to go home to get away from all the fighting and return to some sort of peace. But the rest was determined to fight to keep my independence. I knew something was not right in the Brethren. If they really were the only 'true' church, they wouldn't have to go to such lengths to hold on to their members.

After the police had left, Julie came in with Nigel at whose house I'd spent the previous night. He was a big, burly man and Mum seemed to think he was the Devil in person. An acrimonious argument between him and Dad was soon in progress.

"Religion shouldn't be forced on anyone," declared Nigel.

"It's none of your business," shouted Dad. "Stay out of it."

"You're upsetting Sarah and forcing her to do something she doesn't want to do. A fine brand of Christianity that must be."

"It certainly isn't mine," put in Julie who was a very strong Christian.

Mum threw her a look of hatred and the two men continued to shout at each other until my head felt it was about to burst.

"Stop it," I screamed. "For goodness' sake, stop this senseless arguing over me. Just leave me alone."

There was a shocked silence and then Julie said quietly, "She's right. It's been a trying time for her.

Please leave now and let her make up her own mind what she wants to do."

It was then I realised how strong Dad was. I knew he wouldn't give up but would keep on fighting till I was forced to return home because he loved me so much. But if I didn't go back, the Brethren would say he'd failed. I also realised something else. Dad had rejected his parents and the rest of his family to stay with the Brethren. If his daughter now rejected him and his beliefs, wouldn't it suggest he'd been wrong all the time?

I was touched that he kissed me when he said goodbye. Mum didn't and that hurt me deeply. She'd hardly said anything but she looked at me with such deep sorrow. I sensed she wasn't happy but had bottled up all her frustration; underneath it, I believed she wanted me back on any terms – even if I still refused to accept the Brethren's rules. After they'd left, Julie went to make some coffee and I was left alone with Nigel. It had all been too much for me and I burst into tears again, sobbing noisily. I must have looked a sight and I felt sorry for Nigel who stood there looking uncomfortable, obviously not knowing how to cope with a weeping female.

After a few minutes he sat on the arm of the chair and put his arm round me while I continued to sob into his shoulder. I was glad he was there. Gradually I stopped crying and said a prayer to myself and I felt strength flow back into me. The strength I'd identified in Dad had been inherited by his daughter.

Julie rushed in to say Janice was on the phone and wanted to talk to me. I followed her out and picked up the phone.

"Sarah, I'm so shocked to hear about the pressure that's being put on you," Janice said. "I wish I'd never left you."

"It's all right, Janice. People have been marvellous and...."

"Well I'm dropping everything and coming straight down."

"Janice there's no need – really."

"It's no good arguing. I've made up my mind. I'll see you soon."

She arrived about midnight looking as if she hadn't slept for days. She'd become so neurotic about the Brethren she was sure they were following her. Poor Janice. I felt so sorry she was suffering all this for me.

She wanted to go back to her house so I insisted on going with her. Nigel decided he'd better come too – as an escort. So he drove us back. We should have gone straight to bed but we didn't. We sat and talked till five o'clock in the morning! I felt so close to her as we sat in the sun lounge watching the twinkling lights of the boats on the dark sea. It was a clear, beautiful night and so peaceful.

We had a really deep discussion. Janice said she was an atheist but I wasn't sure I believed her. She seemed to be searching for faith and it felt really good to be able to share mine with her and tell her what God had done for me. She was my best friend and I couldn't bear to think of her going to Hell because she'd rejected Jesus and his sacrifice on the Cross for her.

I was very grateful to her also because she made me think very carefully about my own beliefs; as I talked to her, I realised how strong my own faith had become over the past few weeks. What Jesus Christ had done for me by dying on the Cross was personal and I talked to him as my friend and Saviour. All the Brethren's rules and regulations and all the heartache I was suffering because of them, was something quite separate. I felt so sad they'd come so far from their origins in the nineteenth century when they had tried to return to the simplicity of the early church; they'd succeeded for a while before things went so drastically wrong. It just showed what happened when men started listening to a human leader instead of paying attention to what God was saying.

We didn't get much sleep that night: I was woken up by the phone ringing and staggered out of bed to answer it. To my horror it was Peter.

"I want to come and see you, Sarah. I'll be there this afternoon some time."

I didn't want to see him. I was still angry with him because he'd betrayed me before and I was sure it was he who'd worked out where I was now. On the other hand I knew I had to tell him I didn't want to spend the rest of my life with him.

"All right," I agreed. "I'll see you."

I didn't give him directions. He could find his own way. I knew what would happen when he came because he was incapable of coping with a crisis. At one time he'd promised me he'd leave the Brethren and join me and we'd be happy together. But he didn't. He couldn't face the problems so he'd reneged.

All my life I'd been tied to the Brethren and when I'd finally escaped, I didn't want to be tied again by marriage. I wanted to live my life first and travel before setling down. Then, later, I'd be ready to devote my time to my children and husband without feeling frustrated because I hadn't done anything first.

I felt very apprehensive all morning. How was I going to tell Peter that I had to finish with him? He'd pressure me to marry him and I knew he'd be hurt when I turned him down. It was even worse than I'd anticipated.

When he arrived, we had a late lunch and made polite conversation and then we went down to the beach to talk. The sun was shining, the birds were singing and the sea was calm but my stomach was doing somersaults and I wished the day was over.

Peter grabbed hold of my hand. "I love you, Sarah. I don't care what happens; I'm leaving the Brethren to be with you."

"You said that before," I reminded him, trying to detach my hand. But he gripped it harder.

"But this time I mean it, Sarah. Truly. Look at me." He pulled me round to face him. "I love you, Sarah. I'll never love anyone else like I love you."

I couldn't meet his eyes. What I had to do was the hardest thing I'd ever had to face. I managed to pull my hand away and sat down on the beach; he sat beside me.

"I'm sorry, Peter. I just don't love you the way you obviously love me. I do love you but not enough. We've had a wonderful four years but it's over, Peter. I can't face tying myself down. I'm too young. I'm only seventeen although recently I've felt years older."

"Sarah, you're part of me. You can't leave me." He sounded desperate and I thought he was going to cry. Then he lay back on the sand and closed his eyes.

The silence lasted so long I thought he'd gone to sleep. Then I looked at him and saw tears seeping out between his eyelids. I felt dreadful.

"Please say something, Peter," I begged.

"There's nothing to say." He sat up angrily brushing away the tears. "What went wrong, Sarah? You did love me, didn't you?"

"Of course I did. I still do but not enough to marry you. I don't want to marry anyone yet. I want to live my life first before being tied down again."

"So you'd be 'tied down' if you married me."

"Oh, Peter, you know what I mean." Why couldn't he understand? But I knew he was too hurt at the moment to think straight and I hated myself for hurting him. "What will you do now?"

"Stay here till you change your mind."

"You can't, Peter. I won't change my mind and there's nowhere for you to stay. I'd rather you left as soon as possible." I knew I sounded callous but he was weaker than I was and I was making the decisions. "If you stay, it will only be worse for both of us. The sooner you go away and forget me, the better it will be for both of us."

"I'll never forget you, Sarah." He stood up and held out his hand to pull me up. For a moment we stared at each other and then he quickly kissed me and turned away. I watched him stumble up the beach and knew I'd seen him for the last time. Then I allowed myself to cry. Why was it I always hurt the people I loved? My mind felt so confused. I desperately needed to be loved and part of me regretted what I'd just done although I knew I'd made the right decision. I was still sure that God was guiding my life and that every step I took led on to the next one. One day perhaps I would be able to look back and make sense of it all.

I went back to the house and had some supper as it was quite late. Janice was sympathetic and she was sure I'd done the right thing but I felt very depressed.

"My life seems so bleak. I can't see into the future at all."

"None of us can, dear."

"But most people have some idea. Mine's just a complete blur."

Added to my depression, was the fact that I knew my time in Cornwall was coming to an end and I had no idea what I should do next. I didn't want to go home but I couldn't stay there for ever.

Janice must have read my thoughts for she suddenly said, "Of course when you do go back you must stay with us."

"Oh, thank you." I thought about it. Mum and Dad would be furious if I was staying with someone else in the next road. I'd sleep on it. Perhaps I needn't return yet.

The next day I had two letters – one from Mum and one from Tim. Both pleaded with me to return home and I found my emotions tugged very hard.

'How can you cause such heartbreak here at home?' Mum wrote. 'Please come back to us before the world's clutches get you. We love you too much to let you go. Come home and make us happy again – please, Sarah. Don't let Bill break up our family. I know he is trying to.'

That made me angry. Bill had only been trying to help. He'd told me he'd talked to lots of people about the situation and was in constant contact with Mum and Dad. I could imagine the rows he'd have with Dad. They'd never agree and I was still stuck in the middle.

But her last sentence made me cry. 'I cannot tell you how deeply distressed Dad and I are about you. Please don't be so cruel to us, Sarah. Come home so that we can care for you.'

Tim's letter was longer. We'd always been very close and he was missing me. He was sympathetic but told me, 'The enormity of your decision frightens me as I feel it's not fully your own.' He, too, pleaded with me to go home and promised that no one would put any pressure on me but I knew he couldn't guarantee that. He told me, 'I will pray for you every day and hope that you will find true peace and happiness always and forever.'

By the time I'd finished reading I felt like Alice drowning in her pool of tears. I had to go back. I couldn't let my family be so unhappy on my account. I would just have to face whatever God had in store for me.

Janice found me sitting on the stairs still crying. I handed her the letters.

"I'll have to go back," I sobbed.

She put her arms round me and comforted me. She was so kind. "You'll come and stay with us and see what happens. Try to take one step at a time, Sarah."

I was glad she didn't persuade me to stay in Corwall. I didn't want to go back but the pressure was too great. Within the next few months it was to become even greater.

CHAPTER NINE

✠

HOME AGAIN

*O that I had the wings of a dove! I would fly
away and be at rest. [Psalm 55:6]*

Janice drove me back the next day. We hardly spoke
on the way. I was so sad at leaving Cornwall and all
my new friends but I knew I had to go back to face my
future although I still wasn't sure what it held for me.
I was going to stay with Janice and Bill.

Their house was in the next street to my parents; it
seemed right not to go home just yet as I had no
intention of returning to the Brethren 'fold'. If I lived
with Mum and Dad, I knew I'd be an embarrassment
to them. I had a tiny attic room at the top of the Hawes'
house so I could be by myself whenever I wanted to.

The following week I went back to work. Eileen
was pleased to see me but there was a little reserve
between us because I hadn't taken up her offer to stay

with her. She was obviously rather hurt although she understood why it was necessary for me to get right away from my home town.

I found it very hard, going past my house every day to work and knowing I couldn't return to it. Once I saw Dad in the driveway and nearly called out to him but then I thought better of it. But the string that bound me to my family was tightening and I felt I was being drawn back.

It was Mum's birthday about a month after I returned from Cornwall and I was determined to give her a present. I'd bought her a very expensive dress in a colour I knew she liked. I was terrified I'd see one of my family when I went to give it to her. I hoped I could put it on the kitchen table and leave without seeing anyone.

But when I reached the gate, Dad was working on his car in the driveway. I hesitated and then forced myself to walk up the drive.

"Hullo, Dad," I said. "I've come to give Mum a birthday present."

He didn't even glance up. He totally ignored me. A lump the size of a golf ball formed in my throat. I walked past him round to the back of the house to the kitchen door which was usually open. I turned the handle and walked in. Three pairs of eyes stared at me with unbelief. Mum, Tim and Rachel were sitting round the kitchen table having their tea. I couldn't have picked a worse time to make my dramatic entrance.

"Happy birthday, Mum. I've bought you a present. Hope you like it." My voice was a croak and my hands were shaking as I held it out.

She didn't take it. "The only present I want is you, Sarah. I want you to come back home where you belong."

"I can't do that," I mumbled.

"Grandad's ill. He's missing you. It's all your fault this is such an unhappy household."

There was nothing I could say. Rachel started crying and Tim looked as though he was about to; I knew I would flood the kitchen if I stayed so I put the package on a chair and turned to go. Suddenly Mum leapt up, rushed at me and hugged me.

"Please come back, Sarah," she pleaded. "I've missed you so much."

"I've missed you too." The floodgates opened and I knew I needed my family more than my freedom. Pushing Mum away, I rushed out of the house. The curtain of water in front of my eyes almost made me stumble up the path but it cleared so I could run back to my attic 'bolt hole' and sob my heart out. I wanted to go home to my family but I knew that when I did, I'd never be allowed to see the Hawes again. All links would have to be totally destroyed. I felt I couldn't bear it. They'd been so wonderful to me.

When Janice opened the door of my room, we looked at each other and she knew I was leaving.

"Oh Janice, what will I do without you?" I sobbed, flinging myself into her arms.

"You'll be all right, Sarah. We knew you'd have to go back some time and I realise your parents don't like us very much. Don't worry. It will all work out. You'll see."

"But I shan't be able to see you."

"I know. I'll miss you. But you should go back to your family. You've been very unhappy without them, haven't you?"

"Yes," I sniffed, scrubbing my face with a soaked tissue.

Janice handed me a clean one. "I'll help you pack and remember you're welcome to return here if things don't work out."

We packed up my things and Janice drove me back so I didn't have to carry my cases. She dropped me outside so no one would see her. I hugged her, knowing it would probably be the last time I'd see her. The tears started again but I pulled away and staggered up the driveway with my luggage. Dad was still working on the car.

I dropped my cases beside him. "I've come back, Dad. Is that all right?" My voice trembled.

There was a moment of stillness and I thought he was going to turn away from me. Then his tools fell with a clatter and he put his arms round me.

"Welcome home, Sarah. Let's go in and get Mum to kill the fatted calf."

178

He kept his arm round my shoulders and we re-traced the path I'd taken earlier that evening. Mum, Rachel and Tim were still sitting where I'd left them. They were staring into space and didn't seem to have eaten or drunk anything since I'd left. Mum still had a full cup of tea in front of her.

"Look who's returned to the fold!" Dad exclaimed.

Mum looked up and then she leapt up and rushed at me.

"Oh, Sarah. I've missed you so much."

"So have I." Rachel and Tim spoke together and Rachel added, "Don't ever go away again, will you, Sarah?"

"I won't," I promised. And I meant it when I said it.

It was a wonderful evening – a real family occasion. Mum even produced a cake she'd made for when I came home. It had 'Welcome Home, Sarah' on it in pink icing sugar. I was so touched. She'd never given up hope that I'd return.

But of course, the euphoria couldn't last and the next day we all descended to earth with a crash that must have been heard in New Zealand.

The Brethren found out I was back and the next evening they came round to see Dad. They were clos-eted with him for about three hours while we all waited in the kitchen. The tension in the air was so thick an axe would have been needed to slice through it. When they finally left and Dad came into the room, he was ashen and shaking.

"Oh, John, what's happened?"

We all stared at him as he slumped into a chair.

"We've been 'shut up'."

"All of us?" Mum whispered.

"Yes."

"Even Grandad?"

"Yes."

I couldn't believe it. It was all my fault. Because of me, my whole family was going to suffer the ultimate torture. They wouldn't be able to go to any Meetings, talk to or eat with anyone except the family and they would be totally isolated from everyone. Resentfully, I wished they'd gone the whole way and expelled us all – 'withdrawn from us' as they called it. At least then I'd be a little nearer fulfilling my vow. But I'd still be going to work every day and I had no intention of not talking to Eileen.

The following evening it was my turn. Tony Bates, Brian Forbes and Jack Carr appeared on the doorstep.

"We've come to talk to Sarah," announced Tony Bates.

Mum showed them into the front room and I was summoned. I walked into the room, the door was shut behind me and three pairs of hostile eyes stared, unblinking, at me. I felt as though spiders were crawling all over me.

None of them said anything. They just stared. I knew it was part of their technique but I found it very difficult to cope with it. My legs were shaking so I sat down.

"Why don't you say something?" I muttered at last.

"What would you like us to say, Sarah?"

"Why won't you let my parents back into the Meeting? None of this is their fault."

"But your father is responsible for you. You've let him down, Sarah. You've let us all down."

I hung my head. I felt drained of all emotion. There was another long pause.

"Do you believe the Brethren are the only ones who have the Truth?" demanded Brian Forbes at last.

When I didn't answer, he repeated it – louder and then finally he shouted it at me until I was so confused I didn't know what I was saying.

"Yes. Yes," I screamed. "Of course they have."

It was a lie but to help my family return to the 'fold' I felt I had to say what they wanted to hear.

"Do you listen to music?" A change of subject – again repeated louder and louder.

"Sometimes."

"Ah. How do you listen to it?"

"I've got a radio – but Dad confiscated it."

Perhaps that answer would help Dad. I hoped they wouldn't think he'd been listening to music too!

"Do you have any problems at the moment, Sarah?"

How did I begin to answer that? My life was one big problem but most of it was caused by the Brethren and I was sure that wasn't what they wanted to hear!

While I was debating what to say, Brian Forbes said, "You often don't wear a headscarf. Do you find that a problem?"

What a trivial thing to mention! "Yes I do but I'll try to wear it more," I heard myself promise.

By then I'd have said anything to make them leave me alone.

"Do you have a Bible, Sarah?" Tony Bates suddenly demanded.

What a silly question. "Of course I do."

They exchanged glances. Obviously this was a significant question but I couldn't think why. It wasn't long before I was enlightened.

"Of course it's Mr Darby's translation," suggested Tony Bates.

Mr Darby, who had been one of the founders of the Brethren movement in the last century, had translated the Bible and this was the version the Brethren always used. I found it difficult to understand and said so.

"It's old fashioned language," I complained. "It's much easier to understand God's Word in one of the modern translations in today's language. The 'Good News Bible' is great. It's so easy to follow."

"Great?" Tony Bates' eyes looked as though they were about to pop out and drop on the coffee table. "Oh dear, oh dear." He shook his head in disbelief as his colleagues made appropriate disgusted noises.

Why hadn't I kept my mouth shut? Fortunately my torturers decided they'd had enough of me and Tony Bates said, "Right, we'll speak to your father now."

I left the room and called Dad and it was his turn to be shut up with them for hours.

For the next six months I had 'visits' every week. Sometimes it was two brothers and sometimes three. They went over and over the same ground asking me what I'd been doing, why I'd gone away and why I worked in 'the world'. In the end I felt I really couldn't cope any more. It was as if something inside me snapped and I pleaded to be allowed back into the Meetings so I could worship God with them. I still felt so awful that my family couldn't go out either – and it was all my fault. I found myself saying things I knew I didn't mean just so we would all be allowed back.

My pleas were ignored and then one evening Tony Bates started talking about the 'spirits' in me.

"You're a battlefield, Sarah, with two spirits fighting inside you. You must ask God to help you overcome the evil."

"But I've said I'm sorry for everything I've done. What else can I do?"

They went on and on about the 'spirits' inside me until I was so tired and confused I didn't know what I was doing. I really thought I was in Hell. I couldn't cope with all the pressure mounting up inside me and I thought I must be going mad.

I burst into tears and rushed out of the room and flung open the front door.

"Sarah, Sarah. It's nearly midnight. Where are you going?"

I heard Mum's voice behind me but I didn't care. I ran down the road and into the woods, still crying. I was so unhappy I didn't even care about the danger. If someone found me and killed me, I'd be glad I thought because then God would take me to Heaven and I would be with Jesus in a peaceful place. I wanted that. I wanted to die and get away from this Hell on earth.

There was no one in the woods and I was still alive when I stopped running so God had obviously decided my time to die hadn't yet come. Presumably he'd left me on the earth for a reason. I sat on a tree trunk and prayed for help. By the time I returned home, I was calmer. I had to admit I hadn't really liked the idea of leaving my family and being lowered into a grave – but that would only be my body, of course. The real part of me would be in Heaven.

The next day I felt better and had more of a will to live. I decided there must be some purpose to life. But I was still very confused. I had hours of 'priestlies' every week for about six months and although I kept pleading to be allowed to go back to the Meeting, the brothers wouldn't listen. I think they enjoyed punishing me and by the end I was telling them so many lies, I was no longer sure what was true. It was dreadful I was forced to lie all the time. But if I told them of the pressure building up inside me which they'd caused, they'd say it was the Devil and I'd have even longer 'priestlies'. I couldn't take it. I poured out all my thoughts and frustrations to my dear diary. I was afraid to talk to anyone in case I was found out and got into even more trouble. I'd have liked to talk to Eileen about my problems but I still felt some loyalty towards the Brethen so I couldn't tell her how awful they were to me.

She knew I was having more problems and I was touched when she said to me, "I do admire you, Sarah, for keeping so cheerful all the time. I don't know how you do it."

Nor did I! If only she knew what was really going on in my head. The only one who did know was Jesus and I was so thankful to be able to talk to him. I kept pleading with him to help me but he obviously felt I had to be tested still more before I could be really free. It was very hard.

I was also getting very worried about Tim. He didn't want to leave the Brethren but he said he didn't believe in God. It made me so sad because he was becoming like a lot of the young people in the Meeting who thought it 'heavy' to read the Bible and sing hymns and 'cool' to mock God. I felt there was definitely something lacking in the teaching of the young. They didn't seem to understand what Jesus had done for them.

Tony Bates kept telling me it was the Devil's fault I had run away but I knew it was God's doing. My faith was so much stronger than before and I so wanted to help God to fight the Devil by telling people what he had done for them.

Before one 'priestly' I felt in quite a happy mood but that didn't last long after they started at me. But for once I told them my real feelings so I knew I'd dashed any hopes of being allowed back into 'the fold'. I hated the hypocrisy so I told them exactly how I felt.

"It's awful that I'm not allowed to praise God in a place of worship every Sunday."

"We have to protect the Assembly from evil," said Tony Bates pompously.

"Meaning I'm evil, I suppose. Well evil gets in everywhere and it's certainly got into the Brethren when you deny an old man the chance to Break Bread because of what his granddaughter's done. It's made Grandad quite ill, you know." I was well into my stride now and the words continued to pour out. "The only person who is holy and therefore really worthy of entering the Assembly is Jesus himself. And he always helped people and he was never rude to them."

"Well we're trying to help you."

"No you're not. You're doing the opposite."

Tony Bates changed track. "I hope you don't talk to anyone 'outside' about all this, Sarah. We don't want any publicity. Of course," he added hurriedly, "we've got nothing to hide."

Oh hadn't they? I thought cynically. I'd just opened my mouth to make a crushing reply when I heard the front door open and Tim's voice shouting. I clenched my fists and hoped my interviewers wouldn't realise he was drunk. I heard Mum trying to quieten him as he stumbled upstairs.

I wanted my inquisitors to leave because I was so tired but I decided I'd better keep them talking until Tim had had time to hide. The Brethren weren't teetotallers and they always had whisky in their houses so it was partly their fault but I knew they wouldn't accept that.

They left about one o'clock after talking to Dad for hours. Nothing was resolved as usual.

The next week we heard 'through the grapevine' that Mr Finch, the 'High Priest' who lived in Australia, had decreed that 'young people should get an education'; suddenly everyone was allowed to go on to Higher Education – but not university. That was still 'evil' apparently!

I thought about this for a while and then wrote for a prospectus to a College in the next town. When it came, I poured over it all evening and then half-heartedly applied for a place on a Business Studies Course. I didn't think I'd be successful as I had no A levels and it was a very popular course. But I sent in a C.V. with all my G.C.S.E. results and work experience. I needed to have a change of scene as some of my workmates, including Eileen, were pressuring me to break away from my roots. I felt a change and a new challenge would be beneficial.

When I didn't hear anything, I phoned up and the Head of Business Studies said she was very impressed with my C.V. and they were going to have a meeting about me as they thought I was a 'special case'! She phoned back in the afternoon to say they'd agreed to offer me a place. I couldn't believe it. I knew it would be very hard work but it would keep my mind off 'priestlies' for a while.

I was sad to leave my job but excited about studying again. I enjoyed the course but I found College life a strain. I was still 'shut up' and as I didn't want to jeopardise my chances of returning to the Meeting, I distanced myself from the other students; I knew they thought I was 'stuck up' but it seemed the safest thing to do. I didn't want anyone to ask me questions.

Tony Bates' married son lived opposite the College so I was instructed to eat my lunch in his house. I couldn't share the same table, of course, as I was still 'outside' the fold!

One day I got home after a very good day at College to find Mum crying and Rachel standing in front of her looking embarrassed.

"What on earth's happened now?" I exclaimed.

"That beastly Robin took photos of me and Darren kissing in the woods and showed them to Tony Bates."

"What?" I really couldn't believe they'd sink so low. What made it so much worse was that the Brethren had at last decided we were to be allowed back. Tonight we were to have our last 'priestly' and, because of what

188

had happened, Rachel was the first to be put through the third degree. Mum was in despair.

"As if we haven't enough problems already," she moaned. "Now I've got to go everywhere with Rachel to make sure she doesn't do anything silly again."

I felt really sorry for her and for Dad. The Brethren said it was all his fault because he didn't keep his family in order properly. My 'priestly' was the worst one I'd had. I knew someone had been spying on me too when I was asked if I listened to 'pre-recorded' music. Of couse I lied and said I didn't.

"Do you ever use headphones?"

Then I knew someone had seen me and reported me. I thought quickly and came up with a brilliant answer.

"Oh yes, I wear headphones," I said glibly. "I prepare myself for tests by taping my notes and listening to them as I cycle to College."

Brian Forbes looked disapproving. "Nevertheless, it gives the impression to 'outsiders' that you're listening to music. We have to set an example. You must get rid of the cassette player."

I nodded but I knew I wouldn't. I needed my music.

"You're not friendly with anyone at College?" Tony Bates queried next.

"Oh no." How strange that it should be wrong to be friendly.

I was amazed to find him looking at me approvingly. "Good," he said. "You should always be the odd one out – a bit of a mystery to others."

Yes, that was it, I thought. They went on at me for hours as usual and I felt as though I'd gone over the rapids by the time they'd finished with me and I could return to my College work. I was working hard but I was so lonely. Most of the other students went out in the evening but I stayed in, writing to my only real friend – my diary.

The following evening I decided I had to go out to get some air so I went for cycle ride. I hadn't planned it but I ended up at the Hawes' house and had a lovely chat with Janice. I hadn't seen her since I'd moved back home.

Of course a 'spy' saw me leaving and 'reported' it to Mum. I looked outraged and lied to avoid further trouble. "I was just turning round in their drive, Mum."

I don't think she believed me but she had enough to cope with so obviously couldn't be bothered with this latest 'report' about her erring daughter.

The 'priestlies' continued to get worse. I made a desperate effort to say all the right things so we could return to the Meeting. But I felt ashamed of myself afterwards for lying so much.

"It was the Devil who made you leave us, wasn't it, Sarah?"

"Yes."

"You won't ever do it again, will you?"

"No."

But I didn't believe that even as I said it. I had a vision of myself in ten years' time – Meetings every night, married to a man I didn't love, six kids and spied on every minute of every day. I had nightmares about it and woke up crying and sweating. I wanted to go back for my family's sake but I was terrified about my own future. But I felt it would be God's decision as to whether we were allowed back soon.

Eventually they must have tired of visiting us because Tony Bates rang Mr Finch in Australia to ask about us and he said we could go back. What a system!

So we all trooped back into the Meeting Room on Saturday for a Fellowship Meeting. It was awful. Eveyone was staring at us and whispering.

Afterwards Ruth Bates came up to me and hissed. "What's it like 'out there'?"

Of course I had to lie again. "Awful," I muttered.

"There aren't any Christians 'out there', are there?" she said smugly.

"No." Oh please, God, forgive me, I prayed silently.

I hoped he would understand I had to lie or she'd tell her father what I'd said and we'd all be shut up again. I couldn't bear that. But I wondered how long I'd survive. My feelings about the Brethren hadn't changed at all. In fact they'd hardened.

CHAPTER TEN

⌘

GOD IS GREAT!

Trust in the Lord with all your heart and lean not on your own understanding. In all your ways acknowledge him and he will make your paths straight. [Proverbs 3:5-6]

I was still working hard at College but one Sunday after I'd returned from the six o'clock Supper Meeting, I went to my room and discovered about eight assignments that were due in the following week! I couldn't believe it! How had I managed to get so far behind? What was I going to do?

The sob story I made up to persuade Mum and Dad to let me stay at home for the rest of the day wasn't very successful.

"You are so selfish, Sarah," Mum scolded. "If you stay in, we'll have to stay with you."

"I'm nearly eighteen," I retorted. "Surely I'm capable of staying in my bedroom alone."

"We can't trust you," complained Dad. "You might put some lipstick on when you're alone."

I stared at him. It was all Ruth Bates' fault for telling Mum and Dad I wore lipstick. It wasn't true. I couldn't help it if my lips were naturally red. As if I'd put on lipstick to write an assignment!

"Well if you're so worried about me," I said crossly, "you can lock me in my room."

"Don't be ridiculous, Sarah." Mum had calmed down. "I suppose I'll have to stay in with you."

I only got one assignment done and then fell asleep. I'd had a bad night; that wasn't unusual. I managed somehow to get the other work done the following week and on Saturday we were all going to a car boot sale. I was going to have a stall selling cakes I'd made.

At eleven on Friday night Tony Bates rang up. I heard Dad's side of the conversation.

"Yes we are going out tomorrow........Oh I see......Mr Finch has said.....Yes....Right.......Yes I agree."

We were all waiting anxiously as he put down the phone.

"Well?" demanded Mum.

"We can't go tomorrow."

I exploded. "I've been cooking and freezing cakes and puddings for months so that I could make some money to support myself at College. Why can't we go? I suppose Mr Finch has thought up a new rule that says we can't sell anything to 'worldlies'."

"Something like that." Dad shrugged and walked off. It was all right for him. He hadn't been slaving for months over a hot stove! To add to my fury I'd just removed all the 'goodies' from the freezer and they'd started to defrost. I was even angrier when I discovered all the things I'd baked were to be used for the Brethren. I'd had months of work for nothing!

That night I couldn't sleep so I read the Bible till four o'clock in the morning. I used to think it was such a boring book but as soon as I started reading the Good News Bible in today's language, I found it fascinating. Mr Darby's translation that the Brethren used was so old fashioned and difficult to understand. No doubt that was why the young people treated it with such disrespect. They 'forgot' to take their Bibles to the Meeting and if they did have them, they refused to follow when someone was reading it. I felt really sad about this and wished I could help them understand what a marvellous book it was.

I particularly liked the New Testament which 'updated' God's word because Jesus had come to the earth to 'sort out' all the things that had gone wrong by dying on the Cross and rising from the dead. I found it full of practical advice and thought it was a very 'loving and caring' book.

On week days Dad usually read a passage from the Bible after we'd had breakfast and the following Monday I suggested we should all read a verse and then say what we thought about it.

Dad was startled. "We have to accept what Scripture says."

"That's not always easy when we don't understand it," I said. "I think it would help us all and I'm sure it's good to have your own ideas about things."

"We have to accept what the Bible says and that's it." Dad could be very dogmatic at times. It was very difficult to get him to see anyone else's point of view. Perhaps I was the same as I secretly still had my own thoughts about what I read. I was sure God intended his Word to be understood by everybody. Otherwise he wouldn't have arranged for it to be written, would he?

The day after this argument I went round to see Janice and found her in an awful state because, Edward, who was now eight, had been knocked off his bike by a car.

"It was awful,Sarah," she sobbed. "He could have been killed."

"Is he badly hurt?"

She shook her head. "It's incredible. They took him to hospital but they couldn't find anything wrong with him. They're keeping him in overnight just to be on the safe side." She paused and took a sip of the tea I'd made for her. "You know Sarah, it was really weird. When I saw him, he said, 'It's all right, Mum. I knew God was looking after me, so nothing bad could happen'."

She started to cry again and I put my arms round her. I found it quite incredible that Edward should tell his Mum, who said she was an atheist, that God was looking after him. I did hope and pray it would change her view of things. I could see she was very confused but it wasn't the time to have another 'deep' discussion.

My time at College was drawing to a close and I knew I should be looking for a job. But my future was still hazy. I was unsettled and I seemed to be waiting for something to happen but I didn't know what it was.

Then Brian Forbes phoned up and offered me a job as his personal assistant. I was horror struck.

"Of course you must take it," said Dad. "You can't turn down a brother."

Oh couldn't I? The thought of working for him till I married and then being trapped for the rest of my life made me cringe. I wrote him a letter thanking him profusely for his offer but telling him I'd already accepted something else. It was a lie of course, but what else could I do?

College finished at the end of July and I was relieved to hear I'd passed the course. I felt quite depressed as I walked out for the last time not knowing what the future held for me. I managed to get some temping work in an office but I knew I couldn't do that for ever. At the back of my mind was the offer Aunt Jenny had made when I'd met her. Would I have the courage to go out to New Zealand by myself?

The other thing that was bothering me was that once again Peter was pressuring me to marry him. I hadn't expected to see him again but he phoned me and talked just as if Cornwall had never happened.

"You will marry me, won't you, Sarah? Now you're back and....."

"I've told you I won't, Peter. Nothing's changed. We have so little in common now."

"But I love you."

"I love you too but not enough to marry you. And I don't want to settle down and stay in England all my life. I want to go abroad and I definitely don't want to get married at the moment."

"You'll change," he said smugly.

"No I won't!" I screamed. "Why won't you understand?"

"I understand you're one of the most selfish people I've ever met." He angrily slammed down the phone.

I felt awful because I knew it was true. I was selfish – in a way. But it wouldn't be fair to marry him when I didn't love him enough. Poor Peter. I could have cried for him and I knew it was all my fault. He was so sensitive and I knew he'd be upset for days. Another reason I couldn't marry him was because I knew he'd never leave the Brethren and I didn't want my children to be shackled as I'd been.

About half an hour later he phoned back to say he was sorry and could we meet on Saturday? Mum came in then so I said I'd ring him back on Friday. I knew I had to say no but I was dreading it. I prayed for help to say the right thing so I didn't hurt him more than I had to. God answered my prayer because when I phoned, Peter was quite different.

"I'm sorry I pressured you, Sarah, and I want to say I do understand how you feel. I remember how I felt when I was eighteen and didn't want to get deeply involved with anyone."

I was touched. I couldn't speak for a moment. Then I said, "Thank you, Peter. I really appreciate that. I know I hurt you and I'm really sorry, I hated to do it but I felt it was right."

"I know. I do understand, Sarah. I hope things work out for you."

"Thanks – and for you too. I will pray for your happiness."

I put down the phone and sat on the stairs to have a little cry. He was so nice and I was so grateful he understood and there was no longer any bitterness between us.

I was still wondering what to do with my life. I'd written to Aunt Jenny to ask if I could stay with her for a little while but it was all a bit vague. I lay awake at night going over everything in my mind. Sometimes I decided I was definitely going abroad; at others I thought I couldn't stand the hassle of it all. How would I get the tickets? Who would take me to the airport? Suppose I never saw my family again. I couldn't bear that.

One Tuesday after I'd had a particularly bad night, I saw a terrible accident on the way home from work. A little boy on a bike collided with a car and was thrown into the air in a shower of glass. He just lay there in a pool of blood. I was shaking and crying all the way home and I thought how precious life was and how suddenly it could be taken away from us.

When I got home, I discovered to my horror that Aunt Jenny had written to Mum and Dad. I was really worried in case she'd said anything about me. There was no letter for me so I still didn't know whether I could visit her.

A few days later something awful happened. Jerry, a friend of Tim's, was involved in a terrible accident. His brand new car was a total write off and he was hurt. But the worse thing was that the police had been following him and he was charged with driving while he was drunk.

Unfortunately we were dragged into it because Tim had met Jerry earlier on the evening of the accident. Tim was becoming more and more anti-Brethren and even anti-Christianity. I was worried about him as he seemed to be getting into bad company. Some of the young brothers seemed to be going right off the rails. I knew Tim was always going to pubs and cinemas and I dreaded to think what would happen when the Brethren found out.

Of course they did and the next day Tony Bates and Brian Forbes descended on our house to interview Tim. I listened at the door and was horrified at their method of questioning.

Tony Bates: Have you ever been to a cinema?

Tim: No.

Tony Bates: Now, you know that's not true. You have haven't you?

Tim: No.

Tony Bates: (louder) You have been to a cinema, haven't you?

Tim: No.

Tony Bates (louder and triumphantly): We know you have. You've been seen.

Tim: All right then, I have.

Tony Bates: So you were lying, weren't you? (Pause) WEREN'T YOU?

Tim: Yes.

I couldn't listen to any more and I crept away. I felt so sorry for my brother. The next day it was Dad's turn and he was grilled about Rachel and me. Rachel had started to smoke although I kept telling her it was bad for her; that was one more black mark against us. Another one was that my car had been seen outside Uncle Adrian's house. Dad asked me if I'd been visiting and I was in a quandary. I had, of course, but if I admitted it, we'd all be in trouble. But if I lied, I'd feel very uncomfortable because I'd be lying to God. Whatever I did would be wrong.

Although I wanted my family to leave the Brethren, I didn't think Dad was ready to. He regarded everything that happened as a 'test'. Eventually I admitted I had visited Uncle Adrian and Aunt Rosemary and I knew I'd have to have a 'priestly' so I went out for a long walk in the rain to avoid it. Anything was better than being 'grilled'. When I got back, Rachel told me 'they' were in the lounge.

"I'm not here, if they ask," I hissed. "I'm going to hide in the shed."

I crouched in there for ages, thinking; eventually, when I thought they'd given up and gone, I went in to find Dad. He was in the hall.

"Dad, I don't want to see the Brethren," I said. "I've got nothing to say to them and we go round and round in circles."

He looked embarrassed and the lounge door suddenly flew open and Tony Bates stood there glaring at us.

"It's obvious you weren't 'shut up' long enough last time," he snarled. "You'll all be 'shut up' until you can control your family better, John." He stormed out followed by Brian Forbes.

"Oh dear, I'm so sorry, Dad." I collapsed on the stairs. He'd gone quite white and I felt for him. I was sure he didn't really agree with everything. Perhaps this would be the first step on our way 'out'. I was becoming more and more convinced I would never return to the Brethren 'fold'.

Then my cousin Tessa phoned to tell me she and her brother, Michael, were going to go to New Zealand in December. Was this the answer to my prayer?

"Do you want to come with us?" she asked. "Aunt Jenny says she'd love to have you. She's written to your parents but only generally. She hasn't mentioned you."

"Thank goodness. I was really worried when I realised she'd written to Mum."

"So do you want to come?"

"Of course I do but – it's a big decision. Can I think about it?"

"Don't take too long. We have to book the tickets fairly soon."

I wished I had someone to talk to but there wasn't anyone so I poured out all my thoughts and feelings in my diary. It really helped to sort out my thoughts and of course I prayed as well. I was sure the fact that we were 'shut up' was a sign. When Tessa phoned back, I'd made up my mind..

"Yes, I'll go. Please book me a ticket."

"Great. Don't forget you'll need a passposrt."

Help! Could I get that without Mum and Dad discovering? I would tell them I was going but not yet. I was so excited. I got a passport form from the Post Office and took it round to the Hawes so Bill could sign it for me. I arranged for it to be sent to their house and when it came, I smuggled it out to Tessa so she could look after it for me. I didn't want to risk its being confiscated by Mum and Dad!

Things were, of course, going too smoothly to last! I got home on Friday evening to find Mum sitting on my bed with my diary in her hand. I was furious and snatched it from her.

"You've no right to read my private diary."

"It's a good thing I did. What do you think you're doing, Sarah? How dare you arrange to go to New Zealand without even telling us."

"I was going to tell you," I muttered, "but nearer the time."

"Do you realise you'll be leaving your family for ever? How could you do this to us?"

I started crying. "Of course I don't want to leave you."

Mum put her arms round me. "Oh Sarah, what are we going to do with you? Won't you ever settle down?"

"I don't want to settle down," I snivelled. "I want to have some fun. I want to see the world."

"I know but it won't be easy you know, Sarah." She looked thoughtful.

I dried my eyes. "So you won't tell Dad about New Zealand? Please."

She sighed. "All right but that doesn't mean I think you're doing the right thing, Sarah."

"You're not very happy about things, are you, Mum?"

She shook her head but wouldn't say any more. Later I discovered she'd heard that Jerry's father had thrown him out of the house because of the police charge and poor Jerry was trying to cope on his own in the house he'd bought. Mum was really worried about him and because she thought the way he'd been treated was so awful, she tried to help him. That also contributed to her support for me in my attempt to 'escape'.

The following Sunday evening, I went to the New Wine Fellowship again. As we were 'shut up', we weren't allowed to go to the Meeting and I knew Dad would disapprove if he knew I'd gone to a 'church'. But the presence of God was so real there. I felt a new person and entirely at peace with God. It was so moving to meet with him and feel him so near me. I had a lot to think about. God had been so gracious to me and even when I forgot about him, I knew he hadn't forgotten me.

It was a Communion Service and before we took the Bread and the Wine, the preacher read the Bible passage about the Last Supper. He then reminded us about the seriousness of 'Breaking Bread'. We were told we should examine ourselves and put right anything that was wrong in our lives by asking God to forgive us.

I had a lot to ask God to forgive me for and I felt like crying as I talked to him. For eighteen years I'd been taking part in God's Service of Remembrance without thinking about him at all. I'd just taken the Bread and Wine and passed it on without thinking about what I was doing.

After we'd taken the Bread and Wine, we sang a hymn about God being in the midst of us and the Holy Spirit walking with us. Never before had I been so aware of the Holy Spirit within me. It was such a living feeling. Before, I'd always treated God as a friend but now I realised how almighty he was. I prayed earnestly that his Spirit would never leave me and that the Brethren would be helped to find the right path again.

Of course things at home still weren't sorted out and on the following Saturday we had another tremendous argument. It started because I told Dad I wanted to help people in the world before I got married and brought my own children into the world.

"What do you think you can do to help the world?" Dad asked scornfully.

"I don't know yet but I want to do something. When I live by myself, I'll find a way to help others."

That made Dad really angry. "You're not going to move away," he shouted. "You'll stay at home till you're married. The only right place to be is with the Brethren and your Aunt Jenny had no right to let her husband drag her to New Zealand. She's turned her back on the light and so have Adrian and Rosemary. They're wrong."

He kept on and on until I thought I would burst. At last I couldn't take any more of this verbal battering and I almost clawed at the door to get away.

Dad was still shouting at me. "Do you think you can help the world in that state?"

"Leave me alone," I screamed rushing out of the room.

Tears were streaming down my face and great waves of anguish were swamping me. I ran into the woods taking great gulps of air. I was even more upset because I'd felt that God had been helping Mum and

Dad to see the truth. But after the row I'd just had, I felt it had all gone wrong again. Why hadn't God answered my prayer?

But I knew he was still there and he was the only one I could talk to. Then something miraculous happened. I'd always wished I could have more than a one way conversation with him and that night he talked back to me and I realised he still had a plan for my life and he was still guiding me.

Dad always kept on at me about the Bible verse 'obey your parents'. I was sure God didn't want me to stay with the Brethren so there was a conflict inside me. Then God showed me that in this case it was my Heavenly Father I should obey and not my earthly one. I'd never thought of that before. I walked for about an hour and I was talking to God all the time and he was talking to me. I felt really close to him. It was dark but the stars shone in a midnight blue sky. It was so beautiful.

"Oh God, why does such beauty have to be spoilt by evil?" I groaned.

He reminded me that one day all those who believed his Son had died on the Cross for them would be taken to Heaven and the Holy Spirit would no longer be on the earth to hold back the evil. Evil would then totally engulf the world before God finally destroyed it and then there would a 'new Heaven and a new earth'. I smiled as I remembered the vivid passage in the book of Revelation describing that.

The following Sunday I persuaded Rachel to come with me to the New Wine Fellowship. We told Mum and Dad we were going for a long walk but it was a lie.

As we sat in the Church, I didn't feel quite right. There was a barrier between me and God and as the service progressed, I realised why. The preacher was young and the love of God shone out from him. He talked about sin and I knew his word was especially for me. To stay with the Brethren I'd had to lie all the time and say the things I knew they wanted to hear. Then I got frustrated because I felt God wasn't listening to my prayers.

The preacher said that if we consciously sinned, God didn't listen to our prayers. When he said that, I felt I never wanted to sin again and I resolved to put right the wrong I had done by telling lies. Afterwards I talked to the preacher.

"I've sinned by coming here," I sobbed. "I lied to my parents but it feels so right to be here."

"It's not right to lie, Sarah," he said gently, "but I can see you've got a problem. Let's pray about it, shall we?"

Rachel and I knelt down and he prayed for us and our family. I knew his prayer went straight to God and was heard. Afterwards I felt refreshed – a totally different person.

"I can't lie any more," I said to Rachel as we walked home. "I'm going to tell Mum and Dad where we've been."

"Yes, we have to," agreed Rachel.

It was my responsibility because I'd persuaded her to come with me.

When we got home, I said to Dad, "Can I see you and Mum in the front room? There's something I want to tell you."

My heart was beating loudly and I was frightened but I said a quick prayer and felt calmer.

"I'm very sorry but we lied to you today. We didn't go for a walk. We went to a service at the New Wine Fellowship."

"You what?" Dad spluttered.

"I'm sorry, Dad. I know I shouldn't have lied but it was so wonderful and......."

"Did you take Rachel with you?"

"Yes."

"Then you've doubly sinned, haven't you?" he roared.

"If only you'd come with us," I pleaded. "There's such love there. There's no hardness like there is in the Brethren. They're so cruel and don't really care about young people at all. That's why some of them promise not to do things and then do them in secret. I don't think that's very Christian."

"That's enough, Sarah," Dad broke in. "You're a very wicked girl to speak like that. You've no right to go to a Church. You know they're all wrong and only the Brethren have the truth."

"But I don't know that!" I exclaimed. "It's just not true, Mum. Really it isn't. They love the Lord Jesus and worship him and you can feel the Holy Spirit's there."

Dad wouldn't listen. He just kept repeating that the Brethen were right and everyone else was wrong. I was determined not to lose my temper this time.

"I don't want to go to the Meetings any more even if they let me," I said quietly. "I'd rather sleep in the gutter than go along with things that I know are wrong."

I was amazed to hear myself saying this. I had no idea how I'd live when I returned from New Zealand but I was still praying that God would work a miracle so that Dad and Mum would leave the Brethren too and not disown me.

Suddenly Dad said, "Let's pray together."

I started to cry as we all knelt down together as a family—Mum and Dad, Rachel and Tim. It was the first time we'd ever done that. It felt like a farewell to all those I held so dear. I knew God was telling me it was right for me to go to New Zealand but at the moment I saw no signs of Dad softening his attitude. I felt my trip would be a turning point in my life. When I returned, I'd be dropped into the big wide world, alone, with no family to support me. Dad now knew I was going to New Zealand. He'd tried to force me to change my mind but I was adamant and in the end he had to accept it.

The next two weeks rushed by and suddenly it was time to leave. I was certain I was doing the right thing but I was very sad at leaving my family. Would I ever see them again? I had to stop thinking like that or I would cry all the time.

Mum said she'd drive me to the airport. I was very grateful but I thought it might be rather embarrassing for her to meet Uncle Adrian and his familiy. She hadn't seen them for fifteen years. I didn't sleep the night before and I was up at five thirty. Although I was tired, I was too excited to sleep. During the past few days I'd been so busy packing, I hadn't had much time to think about the dramatic step I was taking.

I went to find Dad to say goodbye. He was finishing his coffee at the kitchen table. I felt very awkward.

"Goodbye, Dad."

"Goodbye, Sarah. What you're doing is very wrong. Tell Jenny she's responsible for breaking up our family."

I opened my mouth to argue and then shut it again. I didn't want to leave with a row fresh in my mind. I hurriedly kissed Dad and ran out to the car into which Tim and Rachel had just finished loading my luggage. They were coming with us. I took a last look at the house as we drove off to Gatwick Airport and my new adventure.

CHAPTER ELEVEN

⌘

FREEDOM AT LAST

Do not be discouraged, for the Lord your God
will be with you wherever you go. [Joshua 1:9]

"Thanks for bringing me, Mum," I said shyly as
we parked at the airport and unloaded the luggage. I
wasn't sure whether she'd want to come into the
airport. Uncle Adrian, whom she hadn't met for fifteen
years, would be there. Tessa and Mike would have been
small children when she'd last seen them.

"I'm coming with you," she said firmly.

Tim had found a trolley and we trundled all my
worldly goods into the airport. Tessa was standing at
the entrance and rushed to meet us. She hugged me and
then turned to Mum. "Hullo, Aunt Margaret. I'm
Tessa."

"Hullo." Mum smiled but I could tell she was nervous.

Tessa grinned at Rachel and Tim and led the way to the counter where Uncle Adrian and Mike were already queueing at the counter. It was very difficult for Mum but she coped very well. When it was time for us to go, we were all crying. I hugged my family. I never wanted to let them go. When would I see them again?

"I'll write to you," I promised. "Please write back."

"We will."

Once we went through the barrier everything was new and exciting and I couldn't wait to start my new life. The flight was amazing; it was fascinating being on the other side of the cottonwool clouds and I was too excited to sleep. Surprisingly, when we arrived in Los Angeles at five o'clock in the morning, I wasn't tired! It was very hot and we had a beautiful view of the sea from our hotel.

The next day we flew along the coast to San Francisco. It was a clear sunny day and my eyes were fastened to the window with superglue!

"Just look at that, Tessa," I breathed in awe. "I didn't know the sea could be so blue."

"The mountains are spectacular too, aren't they?" Tessa leaned across me as the plane lifted and swooped over the hazy mountains.

"Isn't God's creation wonderful?" I sighed. "Oh I'm so glad I came."

I was still 'hooked' on flying as we started the last leg of our journey to New Zealand. No doubt my lack of sleep would catch up with me eventually.

We arrived in Auckland at nine in the morning and I at last met my cousin Lucy.

"I can't believe I'm really here," I said as we hugged each other in the airport building.

"It's lovely to meet you, at last. I knew you'd come one day." Lucy was rather like her mother, Aunt Jenny.

When we reached her house, I felt rather embarrassed as suddenly we were surrounded by so many people and there was so much noise. Tessa and Mike had slept on the journey but I hadn't had much sleep for the past forty eight hours and I felt as though I was seeing everyone through a pane of glass. I had no idea who they all were. I couldn't even identify Lucy's husband. I'd forgotten she was married although she had mentioned it in one of her letters.

However, I surfaced after a short rest and was able to appreciate the superb view of Auckland Harbour from my bedroom window. It was crowded with yachts. I slept well that night and early the next morning I phoned home for the first time. It was wonderful to hear the voices of my family again. I was relieved when they told me the Brethren hadn't been pestering them about me. I felt God was listening to my prayers and was sure they would leave the system eventually. But I knew it would take time. I just had to be patient.

We spent a few days with Lucy and then drove north towards the Bay of Islands. The scenery was breathtaking. We spent a night at a motel near Parahuki Reserve and I went for a long walk by myself. The path was bordered by a variety of trees through which the sun peered down at huge dragonflies circling round. The only sound was the singing of the birds and as I emerged from the trees on to the edge of the cliff, I caught my breath at the spectacular sight of the small town nestling below me on the shores of the lace-edged sapphire sea.

"Thank you, God, for making so much beauty and tranquility," I whispered.

I felt so serene. All the stress and tension was sliding out of me and I knew again how much God loved me. I rejoined the others and we drove on to Russell where we took a boat trip and met a school of dolphins who were delighted to have an audience for their fantastic display. They followed us for miles and I could have watched them for hours.

We discovered the most beautiful beaches and as we walked along the golden sand, our footprints were the only evidence humans had ever been there. I was drinking in all this beauty like a desert traveller gulping water at an oasis. I'd been starved of beauty for so long and now I was seeing so much of God's marvellous creation, it was even more spectacular than I'd imagined. Standing on a rock, looking out over a deserted sea and hearing only the gentle lap of the water round my feet, I felt alone in the world with my Creator.

That evening as I went to bed some of my euphoria evaporated. I was missing my family. Would I ever see them again or would they be cut off from me as my grandfather had been? I closed my mind to that possibility. I had to trust that God would deliver them from the bondage they were in.

The next day we left early to head south for Wellington and Aunt Jenny. Although some of the route was scenic, I found the journey boring and felt very tired as we drove all day with few breaks. It was eleven o'clock at night when Mike finally turned off the deserted main road and bumped up a path littered with potholes. I clutched the seat in front to prevent myself being flung on top of the driver and then we shuddered to a halt. How quiet it was. I opened my eyes, which I'd closed in desperation, and stared.

In front of us was a huge mansion silhouetted against a starred, moonlit sky. Lights gleamed in some of the windows as we staggered out of the car. I nearly fell into a pothole but managed to recover my dignity before anyone saw me.

Mike had started to walk to the front door when it flew open and Aunt Jenny erupted out of it.

"My dears how wonderful to see you all." I was enveloped in a bear hug and swept though the front door. There seemed to be furniture everywhere. I felt very bemused.

A head appeared over the back of the sofa. It was followed by the rest of Uncle Robert, Aunt Jenny's husband. He stretched out a hand and I shook it. As I took it back, I realised I'd been left a legacy of dust and grime.

"Oh sorry," he apologised. "I'm just fixing the stairs so you can go to bed."

"Stairs?" I quavered, looking up. Above me, to my right, I glimpsed a gaping hole leading apparently to 'upstairs'.

"We're building the house ourselves," Aunt Jenny explained, "but we don't have much time. Robert tried to get the stairs up before you came but he hasn't quite finished them."

"Oh – er – I see." I felt like Alice in Wonderland.

"Don't worry, dear; he'll have them up in a minute and you can go to bed. I'm sure you're all tired. How about a cup of tea?"

"Thank you. I'd love one."

She climbed over the furniture to the adjoining kitchen and I heard water running into the kettle. I looked at Tessa who was nearly suffocating in her attempt to control her mirth.

"Behave yourself, Tess," said Mike sternly.

"Oh dear." I collapsed as well and we gave way to hysterics while behind us Uncle Robert hammered and banged.

"I hope the stairs will be safe," hissed Tessa as Aunt Jenny returned, beaming, with a tray of tea cups.

"Here you are. It's so lovely to have you here. Oh by the way, Sarah, I'm afraid there's no ceiling in your room as Robert hasn't had time to put it up. I hope you don't mind."

"Not at all," I said weakly, avoiding Tessa's eye. I wondered what else awaited us 'upstairs' if we ever managed to get there.

It was about two o'clock when Uncle Robert finally propped his makeshift 'ladder' against the 'hole' and invited us to try it. Gingerly I took the first step. The contraption wobbled but I finally clambered up.

"Your room's on the left," Aunt Jenny called. "Robert will bring your luggage in a moment."

I felt along the wall for a switch. Thank goodness that worked. The room had a bed, a dressing table and a cupboard with no doors. I looked up. At least there was a roof – but no ceiling!

When Uncle Robert staggered upstairs with my cases, I hurriedly grabbed a nightdress and flopped into bed. A few hours later, I woke up, desperate to go to the loo, but I was afraid to attempt the 'stairs' in the dark in case I fell down them! But in the end I grabbed my courage and my dressing gown and tiptoed out. Fortunately they seemed firmer than they had done before and I returned to bed with no mishaps and slept again.

When I woke up, I lay for a while staring up at the rafters. Then a movement drew my gaze to the curtain-less window. A monster was leering up at me! I leapt out of bed searching for my dressing gown. It took me several seconds to realise the 'monster' was a sheep! I made a face at it and it sneered and turned its back.

I sat on the edge of the bed, my heart still pounding. I'd forgotten Aunt Jenny kept sheep. I could see several of them wandering aimlessly around the green pasture below my window. In the distance were mountains and the glint of blue water. How beautiful it was. I was so glad I'd come.

It was the Saturday before Christmas and it seemed so strange to be buying Christmas presents in the heat. I felt very homesick again – presumably because I was living with a family but it wasn't my close family.

I knew Aunt Jenny and Uncle Robert went to a 'Brethren Meeting' but it wasn't, of course, the 'Exclusive Brethren'. I had mixed feelings about going to their Meeting the next day.

"Of course you'll come to the 'Breaking of Bread' with us, tomorrow, Sarah," Uncle Robert said that night as we ate our supper. Before I had time to reply, he went on, "but you won't be able to 'Break Bread' until some of the Brethren have talked to you."

"Why not?"

"We have to be certain you accept the beliefs of our Assembly before you Break Bread. We can't accept anyone at the Lord's Table."

"Why not?" I repeated. "Surely it's between the person and God. How can you know what goes on in someone else's mind? Only God knows. I know I love the Lord Jesus and I'm committed to him so I don't see why I shouldn't Break Bread with you."

"But you're not committed to our Assembly, are you? I'm sorry, Sarah. You can't Break Bread with us until some Brethren have talked to you. I'll be happy to arrange it for you."

"No thank you," I said, my stomach knotting up. I'd come to New Zealand to get away from being 'trapped' in a Meeting and now Uncle Robert was trying to pressure me to 'commit' myself to their Meeting.

"Perhaps you'll change your mind," he suggested kindly.

I knew I wouldn't and I could feel rebellion bubbling up in me again but I forced it down. They'd been so kind to me. In the end I did go with them but showed my independence by wearing a headscarf as all the other women wore hats! The service was similar to what I'd been used to; there was a set pattern but they did read the Bible. However I found it boring. It lacked the liveliness and joy that I'd found in the New Wine Fellowship. How I missed that. But the Brethren were very friendly and welcoming to me and I felt warmed by their kindness and interest.

The following day was Christmas Eve and we went Christmas shopping again and I decided I hated all the hustle and bustle of this time of year. I looked at the faces of the shoppers and wondered how many of them thought about the real meaning of Christmas. I felt so sad that Christ's birthday had become so commercial.

When we got home, the house had started to fill with visitors and everyone was wrapping up presents while Aunt Jenny was trying to decorate the tree and organise a meal. It was a crazy household but so warm and friendly. At midnight Tessa was icing the Christmas cake and Aunt Jenny was making the Christmas pudding!

Christmas in the Porter household was a real experience! I woke after four hours' sleep to find a stocking, packed with goodies, at the bottom of my bed. We stuffed ourselves with chocolates for breakfast! Downstairs, the tree was smothered with presents and we spent the morning opening them. It was my first 'real' Christmas and I was thoroughly enjoying it in spite of my previous reservations.

In the middle of all the chaos, the phone rang. Aunt Jenny waded through the carpet of wrapping paper and unburied it.

"Hullo. Oh Margaret, how lovely to hear you. Yes she's here. Sarah – it's your Mum."

I clambered over the debris and grabbed the phone.

"Hi Mum. Thanks so much for phoning. I was going to ring you later."

"Dad didn't want me to but I insisted. He's very cross with me at the moment because we've got a Christmas tree with presents round it."

"Oh, Mum," I squealed. "How marvellous. We've just been opening our presents. You should see the sitting room."

"I can imagine. I went to see Rosemary and Adrian yesterday and took them a little present. They send their love."

"That's great."

She went on. "Tony Bates had a 'go' at Grandad about you and he really stuck up for you, Sarah. I've never seen him so mad."

"I'm so glad. How are things, Mum?"

"Not too bad." She quickly changed the subject. "Rachel and Tim want to say 'hullo'."

It was lovely speaking to my brother and sister but I was sad that Dad wouldn't come to the phone. I could tell things were changing at home although Mum hadn't said too much. Tears were falling down my cheeks when I put the phone down and Tessa came over and hugged me.

"Sorry." I brushed away my tears. "Dad wouldn't speak to me but Tessa, Mum's put up a tree and they've got presents. She said she went to see your parents yesterday."

"Great. I'm sure things are improving, Sarah."

"I hope so. I do miss them. It's like a great hole inside me."

"I know."

Uncle Robert came and sat beside me. "You should tell them to go to the Meeting Rosemary and Adrian go to. They'd like it, I'm sure. It's like ours."

"Maybe." I was noncommital but I knew I wouldn't encourage them to do that. I knew Dad would probably be happy there because it was similar to the Exclusive Brethren but I didn't agree with all they did. They were too rigid.

"You know you can live with us, Sarah, if you don't want to go home. You'd be very welcome."

"I know. Thank you. It's really kind of you." But I hoped it wouldn't come to that. I wasn't sure what I wanted to do. I still felt so muddled. Aunt Jenny and Uncle Robert had been so kind but their house was so noisy; they always had visitors and I needed tranquility and peace.

On New Year's Eve we drove up to a Brethren 'Camp' that was being held near Rotorua and the Hot Springs. Tessa and I were horrified to discover we had to sleep in a dormitory with several girls we didn't know. Neither were we pleased when we realised there a number of rules we had to keep. We weren't even allowed to leave the camp without permission.

"I hate it," I told Mike in tears when we met up again. "I want to leave."

"Don't be silly, Sarah. You can't leave. It's only for a week. Just try it. Look on it as a new experience."

That was the trouble. It didn't feel like a 'new' experience. All the rules and regulations made it feel very familiar and I felt trapped again. Only Tessa understood and we escaped to the beach to have a 'moan'.

I didn't sleep very well that night as the bed was so uncomfortable; the next day we had 'cleaning duties' followed by a long Meeting after which we split up into small Bible Study groups. That was frightening as I was terrified I'd be asked to contribute. Fortunately, the leader, David, talked most of the time. He was very intense and I was finding the whole situation very difficult to cope with.

It improved the next afternoon when we all went for a barbecue in a nearby park. I decided they were a really friendly crowd after all. I met one chap who talked to me non-stop about cricket! I didn't know anything about it as games of all types were very much discouraged by the Exclusive Brethren but I must have looked interested as he continued to talk.

To my surprise I found the evening Meeting quite stimulating and I started to appreciate the fellowship of this caring group. They weren't quite like the Exclusive Brethren after all.

I enjoyed the rest of the time and was disappointed when it was time to go back. Soon after we returned to Aunt Jenny's, I had a disturbing phone call. I was in the garden helping to clean the car when I was called in.

"I think it's the Brethren," Aunt Jenny mouthed at me as I took the phone.

My heart did a somersault and landed in my sandals. Was I to be hounded even here?

"Yes?" My voice was a croak.

"Sarah Foster?" The male voice was pleasant with a slight New Zealand twang.

"Yes."

"My name is Tom Wells. Mr Bates asked me to contact you."

"Oh."

"They're all very concerned about you."

"Oh," I muttered again.

"I wondered if we could meet. I'd like to talk to you and – er – answer any questions you might have."

I thought about it. I had plenty of questions to which I'd never been given answers. By now, I also knew where I stood. I knew there were other Christians in 'the world' and it would be a good test to see if I could be strong enough to stand against the system that had bound me.

"All right," I agreed.

"Would tomorrow afternoon be suitable?" He was very polite.

"Yes I think so."

He told me where to go and I wrote down the directions. When I put down the phone, I was shaking but I took some deep breaths and went up to my room to write down some of the questions to which I wanted answers.

I didn't sleep much that night; I was very apprehensive. The next afternoon Aunt Jenny kindly lent me her car and I drove off to face my ordeal. I didn't really want to go but I felt I couldn't run away all the time. The problem of my future hadn't yet been resolved.

Mr Wells and another brother met me in the car park of a typical Brethren Meeting room and I was escorted inside for a 'talk'. Once we were seated on the hard chairs the two brothers were quite friendly and they seemed genuine and sincere. At one time I even wondered why I'd left the group but then, like Tony Bates and others, I felt they twisted the truth to make it fit what they believed in. They mentioned some famous

Meetings that had taken place in the 1970s and asked me what I knew about them.

"I've heard the tapes," I muttered.

They looked annoyed. I wasn't surprised. The tapes contained some awful language and I'd found them hard to listen to.

"But that wasn't how it was," they assured me earnestly. "Things were distorted to make them look worse than they were and many Brethren were misled and deserted us."

I sighed. I knew this was what the Exclusive Brethren believed but I felt they were the misguided ones; however I didn't want to get into an argument about something that had happened so long ago. I changed the subject.

"Why don't the Brethren help the world more and try to convert people?" I asked. "After all if they know 'the truth', surely they should share it with others."

"We have to maintain our position. We have to separate from evil."

"But surely the evil is within all of us and we only get rid of it through what the Lord Jesus did. He told us to be in the world but not of it. That's different, isn't it?"

Of course they had no answer to that and the rest of the time was spent pleading with me quite gently to return to the fold. They seemed rather embarrassed about what they were doing.

"I'm sorry," I said at last. "I can't. I think many of the things the Brethren are doing are wrong but I know many of them are sincere Christians and I feel sad the Devil has got in amongst them to disrupt things."

As soon as I'd said that, I regretted it although it was the truth. Mr Wells shook his head sadly.

"I'm afraid it's you in whom the Devil is at work, Sarah."

I shuddered and picked up my bag. "I'll have to go now," I said hurriedly. "Thank you for seeing me."

I ran out of the room and let myself into the car. I drove rapidly until I reached a layby and then stopped to pray for peace to return to me. I felt churned up inside but I was now even more convinced I was right to leave the Brethren.

After that, I kept having nightmares about the Brethren and my brother Richard's face kept flashing before me. I'd wake up crying because I was so sad I couldn't see him and his lovely children. On the surface I was always cheerful but underneath I was so confused. I didn't know where my future lay and I was being pulled in so many different directions. Aunt Jenny wanted me to stay in New Zealand, my family wanted me to go home and the Brethren were urging me to return to them. Tessa thought I should study for some qualifications while Mike told me I should find a job first.

I kept asking God to show me the right thing to do but so far he hadn't given me a clear answer. Tessa and Mike were going to return to England the following week but I'd decided to stay on for a while so that I could see more of the country. When they went back to Auckland from where they'd fly home, I went with them. I stayed for a few days with Lucy, my cousin. It was lovely to see her again and I enjoyed the time with her and her husband.

But I was getting itchy feet and wanted to be off on my travels. I had a little money but not too much and I thought I'd travel as cheaply as I could and use Youth Hostels.

"I don't like you going off by yourself," worried Lucy when I told her.

"I'll be all right. I'm a big girl now and I've got to stand on my own two feet some time."

I went to my room and started to pack. I wanted to travel light and Lucy had said I could leave most of my luggage with her. I tipped my cluttered handbag out on the bed and started to tidy it. A piece of paper fell on the floor and I picked it up.

It was the phone number of a young Swedish couple I'd met on the plane. They'd been living in England and were planning to spend a few months in New Zealand. They were to be based in Auckland and they'd told me to look them up. I stared out of the window, meditating. Why not phone them? I could have a chat and tell them what I'd been doing even if we couldn't meet.

I clattered downstairs. "I've just found the phone number of someone I met on the plane," I said to Lucy. "Do you mind if I phone them?"

"Who is it?" she asked suspiciously. She was older than I was and I knew she regarded herself 'in loco parentis'.

"It's a young Swedish couple. They were going to stay here for a while."

"O.K."

I dialled the number and to my delight heard Carla's slightly accented English. "It's Sarah Foster," I said breathlessly. "I met you on the plane coming over from England."

"Sarah, how are you? We were talking about you the other day and wondering how you were getting on."

"I've had a fabulous time," I said enthusiastically. "I'm off on my travels tomorrow. I want to see more of this beautiful country."

"Where are you going?"

"I haven't quite planned it out yet."

"Hold on a minute, Sarah." She put the phone down and I waited. When she came back, she said, "We're going south tomorrow. How would you like to come with us?"

I couldn't believe it. "Really? That would be marvellous. I'd love it."

"We'll pick you up about eleven. Where are you?"

I gave her the address and hung up, more excited than I'd been for ages.

"They're going south and they've invited me to go with them. Isn't that great?"

Lucy looked disapproving. "You hardly know them."

"They're really nice. They're Catholics," I added hastily.

"Oh."

That was the wrong thing to say, I thought. Catholics and Brethren weren't exactly on the same wave length and Lucy was still Brethren although not, of course, the very strict variety.

"I'll be all right," I assured her as I hurried upstairs to pack. How wonderful I'd decided to tidy my bag at that particular moment. I was sure God had a hand in the timing.

The next day Carla and her husband, Jan, drove up promptly in a large van. Lucy invited them to have some lunch before we left. They were just as pleasant as I'd remembered and I could see Lucy was relieved.

We set off in the afternoon to drive along the windy west coast road to Hamilton past rolling hills speckled with sheep. The scenery was spectacular and that night we slept in the back of the van by the side of a beautiful lake. It was so quiet and peaceful and I slept really well waking early to the sound of the birds.

The next day as we drove off, we started to have a deep discussion about the nature of God. I found it really stimulating and although we didn't think along quite the same lines, I was sure they were Christians as I was. I thanked God he had brought us together. I was sure it was his plan and I'd been very conscious since

I'd first arrived in this beautiful land that I was in his hands and he had control over my life.

Over the next few days I came to realise for myself that the Brethren's view that all 'worldlies' were 'bad' was totally wrong and I decided I would only judge people by what I myself discovered about them. As we journeyed past spectacular scenery, sleeping in the van or in Youth Hostels, I met a variety of people who confirmed my view. My knowledge of the 'normal' world widened and I found the people I met very friendly.

Gradually I became more self confident. No longer was I afraid to join Carla and Jan in restaurants in case I made a fool of myself. Spiritually, too, I grew. My faith was strengthened by talking about it to my Swedish friends and to others I met. I discovered afresh that the most important thing of all was to have a living link with the Lord Jesus and to recognise what he'd done for me. I was desperate to share this with others.

I always carried my Bible with me and one day we decided to climb Mount Egmont which was on the west coast of North Island overlooking the Tasman Sea. It was so beautiful; the day was clear and sunny and snow glittered on the mountain peak.

"It really makes you feel how insignificant man is, doesn't it?" I murmured as we started the climb later than we'd intended.

Ploughing our way through dense bush, clambering over boulders and searching for the path wasn't easy and as we progressed upwards, we also had to cope with snow. About six o'clock it started to get dark and by that time we were nowhere near the top.

"We'll have to camp," said Jan nonchalantly.

I flashed my torch downwards and felt a bit sick. Far below I could see lights starting to twinkle on the distant hillside. We were so high and I was afraid but I didn't want to show it.

"Look – over there." Carla pointed to a dark shape nearby. "It's a hut. We can camp inside."

It was in the midst of bushes and trees and it provided, as intended, shelter for the night. We lit a fire, boiled some soup and ate the sandwiches we'd made earlier. By the time we'd finished, we were all yawning.

"I'm for bed," yawned Carla. "Let's get out the sleeping bags."

We laid them out and curled up. I kept remembering I'd been told the mountain was dangerous and I lay awake feeling really anxious about the next day. Then I thought how weak my faith was. God had looked after me so far and I knew he would continue to do so.

The next day I said an extra prayer to ask the Lord to keep us safe and we set off on our trek to the top. I was tired as I hadn't slept much. It was hard work because the snow was slippery and I had to concentrate hard to put one foot in front of the other as I crunched through the snow. It was very cold and windy and I daren't look down as it made me feel dizzy.

"Here's the Lodge." I heard Jan's voice and looked up. Facing us was an attractive timber building. "We can leave our back packs here and go on to the top."

I looked up at the towering peak of the summit and gritted my teeth. After dropping my back pack, I felt lighter but the climb was even steeper and I was getting breathless and frightened. I followed Jan and Carla for a little way and then, ahead of us, I saw a party of climbers roped together carrying pickaxes and all the accoutrements of professional climbers. We didn't even have sticks to help us along! That convinced me.

"I'll wait here for you," I called out. "I don't want to go any higher."

Carla waved and I watched as they crawled away from me. I did hope they would take care. I was glad I'd come this far. The view was spectacular. I stood high above the speckled cotton wool clouds and seemed alone in the world. I noticed the clouds were seeping in and the peak was becoming blurred.

"Please God, keep them safe," I prayed as I slithered down the snow to find a place to sit and contemplate afresh God's wonderful creation. Having made such awe inspiring beauty, how could he tolerate man and the mess he'd made of the world?

I took my Bible out of my pocket and read Psalm eight verse four: 'What is man that you are mindful of him?' It seemed so appropriate sitting almost on top of the world with any signs of life so far away.

Suddenly it started to snow and everything swiftly became blotted out. The snow fell silently and I felt totally isolated. Struggling to my feet, I shaded my eyes trying to see the Lodge. Where was it? I was disorientated. I didn't know which direction to take.

"Lord, help me," I prayed in panic.

As the wind blew the snow aside, I could faintly see the outline of the building. Staggering, buffeted by the wind and snow, I forced myself towards it and collapsed inside.

"Would you like some coffee?" One of the attendants came over to me with a steaming cup.

"Thank you. A cup of coffee's never been so welcome."

"Awful isn't it? But it'll clear soon."

"My friends have gone to the top. Will they be all right?"

"There are places to shelter. I'm sure they will," she assured me.

But it was three hours later when Jan and Carla staggered in. I ran to them and hugged them.

"I was so afraid something had happened to you. I was praying all the time that God would keep you safe."

"He did. We found places to shelter but we weren't able to reach the top." Carla's teeth were chattering and I hoped neither of them was suffering from hypothermia.

But after a night's rest, they had fully recovered and we retraced our steps down the mountain. We then continued to drive south to Wellington and we all spent the night with Aunt Jenny. It wasn't a success! I'd been so close to Jan and Carla in the last few days I expected Aunt Jenny to feel the same about them as I did. But they were poles apart and they really had nothing say to each other. So I kept up an inane trickle of conversation and I think we were all relieved when we could go to bed.

The next day we headed for the ferry to take us to South Island. I'd been looking forward to visiting the other half of New Zealand. We left early and I stood on the upper deck watching the sun rise as the sea gulls wailed overhead and Wellington slowly came awake.

A few hours later we docked in the quaint little town of Nelson and for the next few days we drove south revelling in the variety of scenery and staying in Youth Hostels. Here I met a variety of people who further confirmed my view that all 'worldlies' weren't 'bad'. I discovered too, that people liked to talk about themselves and I liked to listen.

Abel Tasman National Park left a lasting impression on me. The twittering of the birds blending with the trickling murmur of tiny waterfalls and the roaring of the sea far below created an atmosphere of total peace; I felt I was alone in the middle of a fairy tale.

Further south, Christchurch was a contrast. On the Sunday we went to a Church service but I was very disappointed. The preacher gave an informal chat which didn't seem to have much to do with Christianity. I longed to find somewhere like the New Wine Fellowship.

After lunch Carla and Jan went for a walk and I sat in the central square and listened to a man, dressed as a wizard in a long black cloak and pointed hat, talk a load of nonsense. At one point he started to mock Christianity and I couldn't stand it any more so got up and walked away. Another man approached me selling some cakes and I bought one. It wasn't till he started talking to me I realised he was a member of the Hari Krishna cult. He talked to me about their beliefs but I was very wary.

"You look as though you don't believe me," he said.

"I believe in God," I said firmly, "and I also know that the only way into Heaven is if you believe in his Son, the Lord Jesus Christ."

"Oh we believe that," he said glibly, "but there's more to it than that. You have to follow the right path and chant at the appropriate times and...."

I'd heard enough. There was no point in getting into an argument with him. It was terribly confusing and frightening to think there were so many cults that were attracting people and some of them did have pieces of the truth. I realised how easy it would be for someone who was searching for a faith to become ensnared. I prayed God would always keep me on the right path. As I walked away, I almost felt I was choking with all the things I should have said.

The following day we travelled over Arthurs Pass through the most impressive mountain range I'd ever seen. The morning frost glinted on it giving it a sugary look as if it had been dusted with icing sugar. We left the car and walked upwards past fast flowing waterfalls and bubbling creeks.

Then we drove along tiny roads through mountain passes and gorges. It was so beautiful and each mountain had its own distinctive characteristic – just like people! As we followed the coast road, beside long golden beaches edged with frothy white waves, the sun gradually sank over the horizon casting a wonderful warm red glow over everything.

We spent the night at a Youth Hostel near the Pancake Rocks which really did look like a pile of large pancakes waiting to be eaten. I almost felt my mouth watering. We'd been away for over a month and although I was enjoying myself, I was beginning to get homesick. Jan and Carla wanted to go further south but I said I'd make my way back to Picton where I could pick up the ferry for Wellington.

"I'm going to hitchhike," I anounced.

Carla looked horrified. "You can't do that. It's not safe."

"Of course we can't allow that." Jan was equally horrified.

"I'm sorry. I've made up my mind. My plane ticket expires next week so I'll have to get back. The past month's been marvellous. I've enjoyed it so much. Thank you for letting me come with you."

"We've enjoyed your company. Don't lose touch with us, will you?"

"Of course not."

Carla still looked worried. "Are you sure you'll be all right?"

"I will – really. God's looked after me so far and I know he'll always be there."

That night we indulged in a large dinner as an appropriate ending to a marvellous holiday. I hadn't told Jan and Carla I was running out of money as I didn't want to borrow from them. I was determined to make my own way. I wanted to prove I could look after myself. And I knew why I had to do it. In a way it was a test. I wanted to prove that God would look after me. I'd already discovered that, contrary to Brethren belief, there were some very pleasant 'worldlies' and this would be another 'test' to reinforce this view.

The next day I left early and waved goodbye to Jan and Carla as I set off to walk back along the coast road we'd driven along the previous night. I'd never hitch-hiked before and I was terrified. Few cars passed me. Those that did, didn't stop. Then suddenly a large car going in the opposite direction swerved round and screeched to a halt beside me.

Turning to look at the occupants, I was horrified to see three enormous Maori men grinning at me. They were the largest human beings I'd ever seen and I was very frightened. I glanced up and down the road. There was no one else in sight. It was now or never. This was the test. Quaking, I slid into the back seat of the car and sat as close to the window as I could. I was so tense I was sure the vast man beside me could have broken me in half with one snap of his fingers.

I'd been so busy being frightened, I only gradually became aware of the music drifting out from the cassette player. Vaguely I recognised some of the tunes and realised the two men in front were singing lustily along with it. They seemed quite friendly. Perhaps I needn't be frightened after all. I glanced out of the window relaxing slightly. A round sticker caught my eye and I spent a moment trying to read it. I finally deciphered it.

'God is Love,' it proclaimed. Now I recognised one of the choruses we'd sung at the camp I'd been to. I gave a gasp and turned to look at the man beside me.

"Are you Christians?" I whispered.

"Of course we are."

"I am too. I was so frightened of you."

He laughed. "No need. Where you go?"

"I want to get the ferry at Picton."

"We'll take you there," announced the driver.

"But you were going in the opposite direction," I remembered.

"Couldn't let a beautiful girl like you wander off on her own, could we? Guess the Lord told us to turn round. We're not in a hurry."

"It's very kind of you." I felt very relaxed now and a warmth was spreading through me. God's answer to my prayer could not have been clearer. He would always take care of me and there were Christians who were not and never had been members of the Exclusive Brethren.

For the rest of the journey we chatted and I learnt about them and how they'd become Christians. I told them a little about myself but didn't go into much detail. I was sorry when the journey ended and I waved goodbye to my new friends as they continued on their interrupted journey and I boarded the ferry.

I phoned Aunt Jenny when we docked at Wellington and she came to pick me up. I didn't want to hitchhike again. The 'test' had been passed!

"It's lovely to see you again, Sarah. Have you had a good time?"

"It's been marvellous."

"There are several letters waiting for you. Your parents are looking forward to you going home."

The letters didn't cheer me up at all. Everything at home seemed confused and unhappy. Rachel was always going off with friends to parties, Tim still wouldn't have anything to do with Christianity, Mum had high blood pressure and, Jerry, Tim's friend, was in a really bad way. He was in debt and had acquired a most unsuitable girl friend. And finally, the Brethren wanted to know when I was going home.

I sighed as I put the letters down. All my pleasure in New Zealand had been ripped apart in seconds. I didn't want to go home to face all the problems again but it seemed as if I was needed there. At least I could probably stop Rachel from going to wild parties and perhaps take some of the pressure from Mum.

As I knelt to pray for all my family, I reflected that God had guided my path and helped me to leave the

Brethren. I had been aware of his hand over me on so many occasions since I'd left England and I was sure he'd help me face whatever awaited me at home.

CHAPTER TWELVE

⌘

MY VOW FULFILLED

The Lord has done great things for us
and we are filled with joy.
[Psalm 126:3]

The plane arrived in England on a bright May
morning. I had to remind myself it was Friday. I
quickly got through customs and scanned the waiting
crowds. My family wasn't there! Tears pricked my
eyes. I'd been so sure they'd meet me. Had I given them
the right time? I trundled my trolley through the Arrival
Lounge and debated my next move. Of course they
could have been held up, I reflected.

Then I saw them – my darling parents with Tim and
Rachel – and my heart felt as though it would burst
with joy. But when I looked at Mum, I was shocked.
She'd aged so much. Rachel looked very different too;
she'd had her hair cut and permed. I was touched that

Dad had dignified the occasion by dressing up in a suit. He looked very smart.

I abandoned my luggage and ran towards them, laughing and crying and hugging Mum as if I'd never let her go.

"I thought you weren't coming," I gulped.

"Sorry, Sarah. We got held up. There was so much traffic on the roads. We should have left earlier. Where's your luggage?"

"Over there." I waved at it and Tim and Dad rescued it and wheeled it out to the car park while we followed, all talking at once! There was so much catching up to do!

We talked non-stop all the way home in the car. I gazed out at the green countryside and thought how good it was to be home again. When we reached the house, I quickly ran inside.

"It's been redecorated. How lovely!" I exclaimed.

"Mum did it," said Dad proudly.

Rachel had even tidied our bedroom and that night I enjoyed being in my own bed again although I found it difficult to sleep. We'd talked all day and too much was buzzing around in my head. Mum and Dad were still 'shut up' because of Tim and me. None of us had yet been 'withdrawn from' but I felt it was bound to happen some time. I wished the Brethren would act quickly. I hated this uncertainty and I knew Dad still felt it was not right to leave the Brethren himself.

242

The next morning I woke up early. The day promised to be beautiful and I hurriedly dressed and let myself out of the house. I walked over to the woods where I'd so often gone to find peace. There was no one around as I sauntered along enjoying the beauty of the Spring morning. Bluebells carpeted the ground, daffodils proudly showed off their golden bells and the apple blossom was so beautiful, I could have gazed at it for hours.

As I walked home, I started to worry about Tim. He didn't want anything to do with Christianity and regarded all Christians as 'mixed up' people. It was so difficult to talk to him about it. He hated being 'preached at'. It frightened me to think he might go to Hell when he died because he'd rejected Jesus. Of course, that to him was in the distant future but life is so uncertain. We never know when our time has come and after death there's only Heaven or Hell; there's no in-between stage.

Eventually I decided there was no point in worrying about him. I'd leave him in God's hands and wait for a miracle. But I was sad that Dad had decreed he shouldn't eat his meals with us. When he was home, he had to eat alone in the kitchen. It seemed an awful thing to do but I knew Dad was only doing it because he still felt the Brethren were right and he didn't want to upset them more than necessary.

Tim's friend, Jerry, had gone downhill even further since I'd been away. He was drinking heavily and had no job but I was glad to hear his girl friend had left. Mum had been round to his house where he'd lived alone since his father had turned him out of the family home. Dad had been disgusted over his treatment by the Brethren and I hoped this might help to remove the scales from Dad's eyes so he could see the Brethren as I saw them. Of course they wouldn't leave us alone. When I got back, Mum was looking harassed.

"We've just had a phone call from Tony Bates," she told me. "He and Brian Forbes are coming to see us on Monday."

"Oh dear," I groaned. I felt sick. All the old feelings swept over me. How I wished we were free of them; I dreaded Monday and yet another 'priestly'.

The pattern hadn't changed. I went in first to face Tony Bates and Brian Forbes. As usual there was a long pause as they stared at me. Then Tony Bates broke the silence.

"We were very disappointed you went to New Zealand, Sarah. Who did you stay with?"

"All sorts of people."

"Did you stay with your aunt?"

"Of course I did."

"You realise you might have to leave your home and not see your family again if you continue to disobey."

Prickles crawled up my spine. That was the one thing I dreaded. How I prayed Dad would leave too. If he didn't, my life would be shattered. I said a quick prayer.

"I can't come back," I said. "I don't agree with things you do and I know there are many lovely Christians in 'the world' as you call it."

"But they haven't 'separated from evil'," quickly interjected Brian Forbes.

"Do you really believe only the Brethren will go to Heaven?" I asked, opening my eyes wide.

They looked embarrassed. "Well – er – of course, there are – ." Brian Forbes' voice tailed off and it was my turn to stare at him but he wouldn't look at me.

"So you've really made up your mind, Sarah?" Tony Bates rescued him.

"Yes."

"Then there seems no more to say. Tell your father to come in."

I stood up with alacrity. Poor Dad. He looked really strained as he went in for his ordeal. My heart wept for him. Standing outside the door, I listened unashamedly.

After a pause I heard Brian Forbes snarl, "Why hasn't Tim left home?"

Dad sounded reasonable. "I don't think it's right to push him out. He eats his meals separately."

"It's a matter that needs facing. Sarah is very stubborn too. She's been staying with her uncle and aunt even though they've been 'withdrawn from'. She and Tim may both have to go."

"I can't tell my children to leave. This is their home."

"Well it would certainly help if you could say something to your whole household about the situation and where you stand. You can't trifle with evil because one thing leads to another. After all salvation is in separation. Isn't that right, Brian?"

My flesh crawled. How could they say that? Surely salvation came only through the Lord Jesus Christ and what he had done on the Cross. But to the 'priests' 'separation' from 'the world' was a most important principle. Tim came noisily in through the front door and I motioned him to be quiet. He joined me at the door making a face at it.

Brian Forbes was now in full flow. "As it stands at the moment, this house is divided, isn't it? A house divided against itself can't stand."

I was delighted to hear Dad was now getting irritated. "Yes you said that last time," he snapped. "But what I say to you is that he who is without sin should cast the first stone."

"Let him that names the name of the Lord withdraw from iniquity," countered Tony Bates. They were back at their favourite game of quoting bits of Scripture to fit their views. I couldn't believe that everyone who didn't belong to the Brethren was 'iniquitous'.

Brian Forbes returned to the attack. "I feel the household is in grave danger every moment Tim is still here. It's very dangerous for everyone. But if he leaves the Brethren, he won't survive very long in 'the world'."

Tim made a disgusted face and shook his fist at the door. "Pompous ass," he hissed. "What a load of twaddle they talk."

"Sh. Listen."

It was Tony Bates' turn. "I notice he's got a radio in his car. Does he have one inside?"

"Certainly not," retorted Dad.

"It's on your premises though, isn't it? It may not be in the house but it's in the driveway."

"I've spoken to him about it," muttered poor Dad.

"But is he doing anything about it? Speaking's one thing but doing's another."

Dad had had enough. "Look, Tony, if you're going to come round here every week and grind me down, I'm going to give up. It seems to me you're more interested in pushing people around than saving the household."

"You can't mess around with evil," Tony said sanctimoniously. "If you do, the Devil will get the upper hand. Now, about Rachel. She's been seeing Adrian and Rosemary on her way home from school."

"I'll get Margaret to pick her up," sighed Dad.

"Good. Make sure she does. Well that's about all for now. We'll be back next week."

Tim and I hurtled into the kitchen. We didn't want to be caught eavesdropping. When the 'priests' had gone, Dad came in. He looked embarrassed.

"You're old enough to live on your own now, aren't you, Tim?" he said.

"They want me to move out?"

"Well you have mentioned it yourself."

"I don't see why I should be pushed out. I'll move in my own time. It sounds like a pretty meaningless visit – as usual."

"I just wish they'd withdraw from us all and get it over with," I burst out. "Then we could all get on with the rest of our lives. It's so unsettling."

Over the next few days I felt very depressed. I felt years older than my nineteen years as I seemed to be carrying the burden for the whole family. I knew it was stupid to feel like that but I couldn't help it. Rachel, in particular, needed a lot of care and I felt more like a mother to her than a sister.

I desperately wanted to go to the New Wine Fellowship as I needed some non-Brethren Christian fellowship. But I knew it would upset Mum and Dad if I went as we were still officially members of the Brethren. So we couldn't go anywhere and I became increasingly frustrated. I was sure God still had his hand over us but sometimes he seemed so far away.

One afternoon I went for a cycle ride and found myself near the churchyard where my grandfather was buried. I hadn't been back since I made my vow and it now seemed an appropriate time to renew it. It was so quiet as I wheeled my bike past the graves, searching for the one I wanted. Then suddenly there it was.

I laid down my bike and stood in front of it staring down, lost in thought. Where was my grandad now? Could he see me? Would he know that I'd vowed to bring his three children together? I did hope so. Shutting my eyes I prayed fervently for this to happen. The possibility was closer than it had been last time I'd been there. I was sure it wouldn't be long before Dad severed his links with the Brethren but it was a very difficult step for him.

That evening I had another talk with him but it was useless. I told him I desperately needed some Christian teaching and fellowship.

He looked hurt. "But you should get all the teaching you need in the home, Sarah. We read the Bible."

"I know but I want my mind expanded. I want to discuss Christian things. Please, Dad, let me go to a Church on Sunday."

"Certainly not, Sarah. If you go, you'll have to leave home. I can't compromise my beliefs."

"But..."

"It's no use arguing, Sarah. You know the position."

I turned away. Why oh why was he so stubborn? Why wouldn't he recognise that other Christians had something to offer? I ran out of the room and climbed out of my bedroom window on to the flat roof below.

No on would find me there and I cried and cried until I thought my heart would burst right out of my body. I felt lost and hopeless and even God felt so far away.

I cried until I made myself ill and Mum came to find me and comforted me. What would I have done without her?

A few days later the Brethren came round again demanding to see Tim and me. This was it, I thought. It was. They'd finally run out of patience and they were going to 'withdraw from' us both. We were summoned to the Meeting at which this would happen.

"I'm certainly not going," I announced after they'd left. "I don't want to sit there and hear about all the 'sins' I've committed. I'm just relieved to be out of it."

"So am I," agreed Tim who looked happier than he'd done for ages.

"Come with me to the New Wine Fellowship on Sunday," I said quickly. "Please. I've wanted to go for ages. Now there's nothing stopping me."

"Well...." He looked uncertain and I knew he was still anti-Christian. But I felt he was wavering.

"All right," he said at last, "as long as they don't preach at me."

"They won't."

They didn't. It was such a lovely warm service and it was so marvellous to be back. I'd been starved of other Christian fellowship for so long. I hoped Tim had been touched by it too. At least he didn't do such wild things over the next few days.

Dad had become very quiet since we'd 'left' and I felt sorry for him. He was in a difficult position. Now that we were 'out', he should tell us to leave his house but he didn't. It was also hard for him because he worked for a Brethren firm and if he 'left', he'd lose his job. But I knew he'd started to make plans to start his own business so I was quite hopeful. Things were moving at last.

The climax came one evening in early September. Dad came to the table looking solemn after a long phone call.

"That was Jack Carr. He no longer wants me to work for him."

"Oh John, what will you do?" Mum sounded distraught.

"Start my own business, of course. I've wanted to for ages." He started to look more cheerful.

I was thrilled. That could mean only one thing. It wouldn't be long before the Brethren withdrew from Dad and we'd be a close family again.

It wasn't quite like that! Dad had obviously been doing a lot of thinking and when they came to see him, he was ready for them and Mum was with him. I knew she'd support him in whatever he decided to do. Tim and I, of course, listened at the door.

Tony Bates started by demanding that Dad immediately tell his two older children to leave his house as they'd been 'withdrawn from' and therefore he could no longer associate with them.

"Certainly not," Dad said firmly. "I've no intention of telling either of them to go. This is their home for as long as they need it."

"Then I'm afraid we......"

Dad interrupted. "You listen to me. You've come round here week after week disrupting my family and upsetting us all. You've shown us no Christian love and have only criticised us. Well I've had enough. I withdraw from you. Please leave my house and don't ever come near it again."

"That goes for me too." I barely heard Mum's voice.

Tim and I clutched each other in amazement and hastily scuttled out of the way as heavy footsteps drew closer. From our hiding place we watched our visitors cross the hall. Then the front door slammed.

"They've gone – for ever! Hurrah!" I grabbed Tim and we did an impromptu dance as Dad came out grinning self consciously. I dropped Tim and hugged him and Mum.

"Oh I'm so glad," I cried. "I've prayed and prayed for this. God has really answered my prayers."

We laughed and cried and the barriers finally dissolved around us as we celebrated with a bottle of champagne Mum unearthed from the back of the 'fridge. We talked late into the night and I found it hard to sleep after one of the most memorable days of my life.

The story was not over yet. A few days later the phone rang and when I picked it up, a rather apprehensive voice said, "Could I speak to Sarah please." It was Bill Hawes.

"Oh Bill, how lovely to hear you."

"Did you have a marvellous trip?. We heard you'd 'escaped' again."

"It was wonderful. A lot's happened since I saw you. We've all left the Brethren."

"All of you?"

"Yes. It's only just happened. We're just getting used to it."

"I'm so glad and that will make it easier for me. I've been thinking a lot about what happened and I think I was wrong to encourage you to run off. I'd like to apologise to your father. Is he there?"

"Yes he is. Why don't you come round? Then you can talk to him face to face."

"I'll be there in ten minutes."

I put the phone down, my head reeling. Should I prepare Dad? No, I decided I'd wait till Bill arrived. The door bell rang in under ten minutes. I flew to answer it and hugged him.

"It's lovely to see you again. How's Janice?"

"She's fine. She sends her love."

Dad was in his workshop and I took Bill to him. I was very apprehensive. How would Dad react? I wanted so much for him and Bill to be friends.

"Dad. Bill wants to talk to you." I dithered by the door and then decided to leave. I dawdled back to the house, praying that everything would go well. About half an hour later Dad and Bill appeared, obviously the best of friends.

"Make us some coffee, please, Sarah," Dad said.

"Certainly." I was so thrilled. My prayers had been answered again.

When I returned with the coffee, they were chatting as if they'd known each other for years. I sat with them for a while and then took the cups out to wash them.

The following week was Uncle Adrian's birthday and Aunt Rosemary rang up to ask if we'd all like to go round for a barbecue on the Saturday. I thought Mum would go but I wasn't sure about Dad. He wasn't happy about his brother having left the Brethren so long ago and still had reservations about him.

"Jenny's over here," Mum told us as she put the phone down.

"Oh good. It will be lovely to see her again." I hadn't known she'd planned a trip.

Mum looked at Dad who was studiously reading the paper.

"You'll come to Adrian's party, won't you, John?" she pleaded.

He shook his head. "No, I don't think so."

"You don't mind if we go, do you, dear?" asked Mum.

"No. You go."

It was a warm September evening as we sat around chatting. The atmosphere was a little tense at first. Mum hadn't seen Aunt Jenny for years. But gradually the tension slackened and I was happy to see most of my family together. How I wished Dad had felt able to come.

Suddenly I heard a car stop outside. "I wonder who that is." Aunt Rosemary looked puzzled. "I thought everyone was here."

We all looked towards the gate. There stood Dad – alone. My heart almost stopped. He'd come after all. The silence seemed to go on for ever. At last Aunt Rosemary broke it.

"Go and meet your brother, Adrian," she said quietly.

Uncle Adrian walked down the path towards Dad and my heart overflowed with happiness as they embraced and walked back towards us. When Aunt Jenny stood up and joined them, I thanked God for answering my prayers. My vow had been fulfilled. Grandad's three children were again together. We were out of the tunnel and wherever God led us in the future, I knew he would always be with us.